Born Out Of Wedlock

by Drew Carruthers

Published by TWH Publishing;
Independent Publishing House, West Yorkshire
www.thewritinghall.co.uk

Cover design by Acepub

This book is a work of fiction and, except in the case of historical fact, any resemblance to actual persons, living or dead, is purely coincidental. A record of this book is available from the British Library.

ISBN 978-1-9164675-0-7

Printed in the UK by Grosvenor Group Ltd, Loughton, Essex IG10 3TS

To my three sisters Elma, Helen and Ann

My two Cousins Teresa and Alex.

Gilly, my International Playgirl

*No individual has any right to come into the world
and go out of it without leaving something behind.*
- George Washington Carver

TABLE OF CONTENTS

PREFACE

Why did I start writing 'my book'? I guess the inspiration for it began when I was sitting in the kitchen relaxing with my grandchildren. My granddaughter was blaming my grandson, and vice versa, for upsetting their parents earlier that day.

Unwittingly, my grandson said the wrong thing. I think he did not mean to say anything out of place, but it did hurt me. My coffee had gone cold and I was just about to drain the cup when he said, "Grandad, you have to realise that you are old, and you were different to me when you were young."

I think that he meant that I was from a different generation. However, he was correct in one way, because I was different to other children when I was born. I was illegitimate.

It was shameful in 1941 to bear a child outside marriage, both mother and child were stigmatised when it happened. Today, most people don't give illegitimacy a second thought.

The following pages reveal my story of being unloved and unwanted while growing up in a village community dominated by the Kirk. Having suffered discrimination because I was illegitimate by those that should have loved and respected me, I took the most obvious option. With the hope of improving my life, I left home at 15 years old and joined the military, only to discover more discrimination, bullying and abuse.

Some of the people and place names have been changed because I have forgotten them. In some cases, the changes were deliberate.

PART 1

CHAPTER 1

The Birth

I was on my way to do something that I had been telling myself to do for the past fifty years. I was on my way home, but I wasn't going back there to live. What compelled me to be driving from Yorkshire to Scotland at breakfast time on a horribly wet day? It was some news that had shocked me. On Facebook, the bombshell had been dropped: Cummertrees church was up for sale.

After what seemed like hours of driving my wife's bright-yellow Peugeot 107 and wondering what I was going to find when I got there, I finally left the motorway and crossed the border at Gretna. A feeling of relief and happiness welled up inside me as I passed the 'Welcome to Scotland' sign.

The rain had eased by the time I turned left onto the A75. As I passed a dilapidated sign that read 'Gretna Football Club' I wondered how a town of four thousand inhabitants could have produced a football team that had, a few years earlier, contested the Scottish Cup Final. Dismissing this thought, I continued towards Annan.

Twenty minutes later, I passed Annan High Street. Not much had changed. There were now two sets of traffic lights and the old police station had been replaced with a tourist shop. Everything else looked pleasingly familiar.

As I passed the war memorial, which dominates the town centre, I saw a hundred horses setting off to ride the Marches. A tear ran down my cheek as I envisioned a thousand pipers, piping 'Scotland the Brave,' led by the coronet and his lass.

More memories came flooding back to me as I crossed the River Annan. The tide was out, and this led me to think about the fishing nets that once dotted the coastline of the Solway Firth between Gretna and Powfoot. After another quarter of a mile I arrived at the junction of the High Road and the Low Road. I turned left onto the Low Road and headed towards my destination three miles away.

I could see Cummertrees in the distance and my excitement became intense as memories bombarded my mind. As I passed the two-room primary school that I had attended, I visualised the twenty or so children sitting in the classroom listening to Mr McLean and writing on their slates.

Next to come into view was the dominating row of fifteen red brick three-storey terraced houses that overlooked the Solway Firth. They had been built in 1905 to attract businessmen and holiday-makers to the area. At the end of the row was the new cemetery. I did not have time to think about any of the people that occupied the posh red houses, because I'd briefly parked the car and walked into the cemetery. There, I gazed at and studied my mother and father's headstone, situated just inside the grounds at the side of the road. I stayed a while …thinking about the past.

Passing under the railway bridge, my excitement suddenly changed from elation to despair. The old bench at the edge of the beautiful lake, where my grandfather used to sit and chat to his retired railway worker friends, was still there, but the lake had gone. In its place was an overgrown mess. One beautiful, nostalgic memory had been shattered.

I was now within two hundred yards of my final destination, which was hidden by the roadside trees and a hill in the road. The old holly tree, on the right of the road, was still there; and behind it, what used to be Hardy Wright's greyhound kennels. The terraced row of twenty-seven whitewashed stone cottages quickly came into sight. I felt as if the Peugeot had a mind of its own as it seemed to slow down by itself. I pulled in to the left and came to a halt. I was at my destination, Cummertrees Church, which was exactly opposite the old holly tree.

******

Cummertrees is where I was born and lived for most of my school years. By the time I was eight years old, I realised that I was different to other children. I did not know why I was different, but it was apparent that some people's attitude to me was not normal. Often, I would hear whispering behind my back; some parents would call their children away from me and my father treated me differently to my sisters. It was not until shortly after my grandfather died, when I was 14 years old, that I found out why – the truth behind this behaviour.

A few weeks after my grandfather's funeral, I called at Jessie McDougall's house. She had lived next door to my grandfather and was my mother's best friend. It was a Saturday and I expected her two children to be home. Jessie's husband, Jock, was in the garden, so I stopped to say hello to him. He told me that only Jessie was at home; Tommy and Christine had gone to town and would not be back for a few hours. He asked me to tell Jessie to make him a sandwich and mug of tea, as he did not want to break off from his digging. I did as he asked and when Jessie made the sandwiches, she included me. I took Jock his sandwich and tea and told him I was going back inside to eat my sandwich.

When I returned, Jessie seemed pleased to see me. We chatted about school and my earlier visit to Belfast to play football. She was happy to hear that I was doing well at sports. After finishing my sandwich and lemonade, it was time for me to leave. I looked at my empty plate and glass and I think she sensed that I wanted to stay and talk. She asked me, "Are you missing your grandfather?"

I told her that I was and started to cry. She gave me time to grieve, saw that I had calmed down, then asked, "Are you happy now that you're back living in the village?"

I told her that I was alright, but that I felt unloved and unwanted. I had heard rumours that my father was not really my father, and I felt that he did not love me. I asked her if she knew whether the gossip was true.

Looking a bit shocked, Jessie told me that I should discuss this with my father. I told her that I did not want to do that and blurted out, "I just want to know if it's true." She got me another glass of lemonade and said, "I'll be back in a minute." As I played with the crumbs on the table, I was thinking that perhaps I should leave, but I decided to stay.

Five minutes later, she returned carrying Jock's empty cup and plate. She put them into the sink along with our cups and plates then came and sat next to me. She said to me, "It's about time you knew the truth." From her story, this is what I learnt.

******

1941 had been a year dominated by war on the continent of Europe. A large number of young men were away fighting the enemy; people feared the end of the world and the government was trying to maintain high morale. It was a time when those that were able enjoyed life whenever, and as best as, they could.

September 8th of that year fell on a Monday. It was the 251st day of the year and at precisely 6:45p.m. I was born at Number Two Railway Cottages in the village of Cummertrees. My mother, 17-year-old Elizabeth Margaret Carruthers, better known to her friends and family as Madge, gave birth to me.

There was no midwife available, so Jessie and Barry Miller, who lived in the other cottage next door, had helped with the delivery. It had been a difficult birth and when Jessie had asked, "Are you alright?" she sensed that Madge was going to be upset. Jessie had told her not to worry; she had a beautiful son and everything would be fine. I may have been a beautiful baby, but I had been unplanned and was unwanted.

When Madge had been forced to tell her father that she was pregnant, he had lost his temper and showed his anger in a way that she had never experienced before. He had trusted his daughter to be sensible and careful by permitting her to go to the local dances to meet other people. He had hoped that by allowing her this freedom, she would meet the right boy, would settle down, get married and come and live with a new husband at the cottage. This was not going to happen.

My grandfather, whose name was Alex but who everyone knew as Barney, was a Kirk man. Despite his beliefs, he had told Madge that she should go to the city with Jessie for an abortion, even though he knew that an abortion would be illegal and dangerous. During his time working on the railways, he had seen girls board a train with a parent or friend to go to the city for an abortion. They had returned a week later, not looking as healthy as when they left. His workmates, Jessie's husband being one of them, commented, "There's another one returning from the terminator."

As the weeks passed, Barney had mellowed and confided in Jock. He had put the thought of an abortion out of his mind. He had decided he would rely on God and the fact that he had read in a newspaper article that the death rate of 'illegitimate' children was twice that of 'legitimate' children. With the war raging in Europe, hard work, and lack of a stable food supply, it might mean that there was a very good chance I would not be born.

Since my birth, only Jessie, Barry and Madge's brother Jim came to see my mother. Jessie visited her every day. She would prepare food, clean, wash the bedding, and do the jobs Madge had been doing before her advancing pregnancy had forced her to stop.

One day, she had called to check on Madge and me and was just about to leave when she heard the click of the latch on the bedroom door. Barney entered the room dressed in his heavy denim work overalls, with his pipe sticking out from one of the pockets on the bib and his two-inch leather belt around his waist. Two people followed him in to the bedroom. Barney ignored Jessie and spoke to Madge for the first time since my birth.

"This is Annie Armstrong from Powfoot," he announced. "She's come to do the registration." Jessie recognised the woman as she was the person who had registered the birth of her own two children. Barney turned, brushed past her and Madge's brother Jim, and went back into the living room. Jim turned to follow his father and said, "If there is anything you need, knock on the door and I'll come back."

Before he left the room he paused and asked Annie if she would like a cup of tea. He did not ask his sister or Jessie if they would like one too. Annie replied, "No, if there is anything I will call you."

It was clear to Jessie that the registrar was uncomfortable with Barney and Jim's behaviour. It was obvious to her that neither of them was going to witness the registration. When Jessie asked if she should stay, the registrar asked her if she would act as a witness and Jessie readily agreed.

When the room was clear, and Annie was sure she could not be heard by anyone in another room, she turned to Madge and gave her a smile. Tears started to appear on Madge's cheeks as Annie crossed the room, sat on the bed and hugged her. When the tears stopped, Annie told her there was nothing to worry about, the paperwork would only take a few minutes and then she could get back to resting and enjoying her beautiful baby. Annie told her not to be concerned as she would soon recover from the birth and be ready to go out into the world again – "That is, if the war does not destroy it first!"

The registration process was straightforward. Annie filled in all the details from memory, except for the infant's and the father's name. Back in July Madge had made her mind up to name me Alexander Andrew, after her father and the patron saint of Scotland. She would use the middle name and shorten it to 'Drew'. She liked that nickname. She knew that if she called me Andrew, quite quickly, people would start to shorten my name and I would become Andy, which she hated. Annie spoke only to say that she thought it was a nice name and entered Alexander Andrew on the registration form. She then asked, "What's the father's name?"

Madge, quickly and firmly, replied, "I'm not saying."

Annie turned to Jessie and asked her if she knew the father's name. Jessie shook her head. The registrar looked at Madge then Jessie and said, "I'll be back in a minute."

When Annie had left the room, Jessie could hear the conversation through the partially-open door. Barney, Jim and Annie were having a heated discussion. Looking perplexed and slightly annoyed, Annie returned, and the final column was filled in: 'Father Unknown.'

******

As the story unfolded, I started to feel depressed, but at the same time, excited. I wanted to know more. As Jessie went into the kitchen to make some tea, I tried to picture my grandfather. All I could see was a kind old man, who used to sit on the bench at the bottom of the path, chatting to his retired workmates. A man who gave me pocket money and bought me crisps and sweets when I pleaded with him. He had taught me how to catch rabbits, grow vegetables; he fed, clothed, looked after and protected me, until he was no longer able.

I also tried to understand why my mother would not tell anyone my father's name. Could it have been because he was already married? Maybe he was away, fighting in the war? Jessie came back with two mugs of tea; she sat down next to me and continued her story.

Madge was a regular Sunday school and church-goer; she wanted me to be christened in the church and had asked Reverend Cowie. He refused to christen me in Cummertrees Church, but agreed to christen me at the Manse. Madge knew that her father would never approve of this ritual ceremony taking place in the church where his family attended services. He had told her when she fell pregnant that her child would be born out of wedlock and, as far as he was concerned, the child would be a 'bastard child'. He told her that I would have no right to the family name or to the family's place in the Kirk. My mother wanted a church christening so declined the offer of a ceremony in the Manse. Perhaps too, she did not want to upset her father any more than she had done already.

Instead of the family's church, Jesse arranged to have me christened at the Old Parish Church in Annan. This was not straightforward as, at first, Reverend Dobie had refused, saying that Madge was not one of his parishioners and she should ask her own minister to christen the child. Jessie lied and told him that Madge had only just moved to Cummertrees and that her family had been parishioners of his church when they lived in Annan. When the reverend asked why Madge or her husband had not come to make the arrangements, Jessie lied again. She told him that Madge was unwell, and that her husband and brother were away fighting in the war and her father was old. Reverend Dobie finally agreed to do the christening.

Jessie was relying on the fact that Carruthers was a common name and, if the reverend checked the church records, he would find that several families with the name of Carruthers were members.

My christening took place in the Old Parish Church, which dated back to 1171, and was built during the reign of Robert the Bruce. On the morning of Sunday, the 14th of December, the church was only half-full, mostly with women and young children. Jessie and Madge took their seats on a pew at the front of the church.

Three baptisms took place that Sunday. Betty Connolly and her young farmhand husband's son was first. The Connollys had several family members and friends supporting them, all grinning like Cheshire cats. Reverend Dobie said a short prayer, sprinkled the holy water over the baby boy's head, and christened him David James Connolly.

After giving David back to his mother, he turned to Irene Jackson, who had been in Madge's class at school. Irene was not thinking about Madge or the baptism, she was thinking about Adam Jackson, her young husband. After completing his apprenticeship as a joiner, Adam had been drafted into the army as a foot soldier. He completed eight weeks of training and was sent to the front line of war. This rookie soldier, who saw very little action, was killed during an enemy attack. He never saw his newborn daughter. Reverend Dobie asked the congregation to join him in a short prayer for Adam before quietly and carefully baptising Jennifer Moira Jackson. Irene was too upset to hold baby Jennifer, so Reverend Dobie placed the baby in the arms of Irene's mother.

Without any comment or smile, Reverend Dobie turned to Madge and took me from her. Following a short prayer, he carefully laid my head over the font and christened me Alexander Andrew Carruthers. After returning me to my mother, he turned to the congregation and quietly said, "Tea is now being served in the Ante Room." Madge and Jessie did not join in with the celebratory christening tea. They turned and quickly left the church without saying a word. Neither of them was ready for a public celebration. They were sure a 'bastard' child would not be welcomed in that community.

CHAPTER 2

The Marriage

Jessie seemed aware that my inquisitiveness was growing. I had listened to the story of my birth and I now wanted to know what had happened after I was born. I asked her, "Why do I have the same name as my father, if he's not my real father?" Jessie replied that it had been a coincidence, "Lots of people around this area have the surname Carruthers. Just count how many you know at school who have your surname." I nodded my head in agreement. She continued her explanations about my history. Barney had threatened to put me up for adoption, or worse still, put me into a children's home if my mother failed to find a husband quickly.

When Madge told Jessie about the threat, she responded by saying it was time my mother started to socialise again. Jessie said she would never find a father and a home for me by staying in and slaving for her father and her two brothers. "We're in luck," said Jessie. "There's a dance at Victoria Hall in Annan this Saturday. Get your best dress washed and ironed!" She spoke to Jock who agreed to the plan. He advised Jessie that he should be the one to approach Barney. "I'll get him to agree to the outing," said Jock. Madge felt elated; she had not been out since she told her father she was pregnant.

It wasn't difficult to get Barney's agreement, as he also realised that my mother would never find anyone to marry if she didn't go out. People in the parish were talking about his wayward daughter behind his back and he knew that this gossip would continue until she was married. Once she had tied the knot, he knew that his and her problems would be over and he would feel comfortable and free to enter the Kirk again.

I asked Jessie, "Why did people go dancing when we were at war?" She told me that entertainment, which was controlled by the government, was seen as 'normality' by parliament and the general population, and a sign that all was well in the war. It was also used to keep up morale among the population – especially when the war was not going as well as the government wished. Very few people could get their pleasure, or news about the war, from television, which had been invented in the 1930s, as not many had the spare cash to afford one. Most people relied on the cinema for news updates – where Pathé News kept people informed, or possibly disinformed, on how the war effort was going. Dancing was seen as the best way that people could forget the war for a few hours and enjoy themselves.

I was excited and wanted to know more. I asked, "How could you afford to go out dancing when you had no money? Did you dress up and look beautiful?"

I could not remember seeing my mother dressed up and wanted to know what she looked like. My questions seemed to bring back fond memories for Jessie. She smiled and said, "Let me get another cup of tea and I'll tell you."

I was left thinking about my mother's situation and my memories of her, my father and my grandfather. When she returned, Jessie seemed relaxed and ready to describe in detail the night she and my mother went dancing. I think at the same time, because I was 14, she wanted to give me a lesson about girls.

Earlier that day, Madge had washed her hair and put it up in rollers. At 6:45p.m., the men headed for the pub and Madge went next door to get ready in Jessie's house for the dance. Having washed her hair in the morning and after setting it with wave gel and rollers, she only needed Jessie to style it. Madge had not had her hair cut in almost a year, so it was long enough for Jessie to style the curls close to the top of her head, so that they fell towards the nape of her neck.

They did their make up together, starting with their eyebrows. Jessie had plucked hers into a thin line, but Madge did not want her father to be upset by this fashionable style, so she just tidied them up and plucked them a little thinner. Madge chose orchid eyeshadow from the little metal box, while Jessie chose a shimmering blue. They shared the ivory and pink foundation powder. Finally, Madge opted for a bright-red lipstick, while Jessie chose a light rose colour. After eyeing each other up, they decided that the end result was perfect – beautiful.

Madge had no problem getting into her girdle, as her weight had gone back to what it was before she gave birth. Luckily, her clothes were still fashionable and fitted perfectly. The elasticised girdle was one that could be pulled directly over the hips. It felt a bit tight, but showed her figure off nicely. As she pulled on a pair of her old silk stockings, she was pleased to see that there were no snags or holes in them as she attached them to the suspenders hanging from the girdle. Carefully, she slipped on her white underskirt and slid into her blue-flowered dress with shoulder pads that sported an open shirt neck and was fastened with a plain blue belt. Finally, Madge applied cornflower blue nail varnish that perfectly matched her dress, while Jessie applied a pale rose varnish that complemented her outfit. All that remained for Madge was to put on her flat black shoes and black raincoat. Perfumed and powdered, they were ready in plenty of time to catch the 7:50p.m. bus to Annan.

I was fascinated. I had seen films where the stars got dressed up and I knew what women might wear to enhance their figures. All I could think was that my mother and Jessie must have looked like film stars.

Jessie paused and then continued to answer my questions. I wanted to know if the dance was expensive, if anyone knew about me, and whether my mother enjoyed herself. Jessie smiled and said, "By the time we got off the bus and crossed into Bank Street, we could see about twenty girls lining up to get into the Victoria Hall. If you got there within half-an-hour of opening time, women were allowed in free, then half price after that. We had one shilling and six pence between us. We knew that if we were careful we would not need to spend any of it. The cloakroom ticket for our coats should have cost a penny, but we did not have to pay that as the girl on cloakroom duty was a friend. So, the whole night only cost us our bus fare."

The dance hall was cold and half-empty, because the men were still at the pub. This was normal; men were expected to drink in pubs, but respectable women were expected to consume alcohol only on special occasions. Madge knew several of the women in the hall as she had been to school with them. None mentioned or enquired about a baby, or asked why they had not seen her for the past year. By nine o'clock, the hall had started to fill up with young men dressed in baggy trousers, jackets, white shirts and plain-coloured ties, the fashion of that era. All the men wore brown or black laced shoes to match the colour of their jackets and trousers.

The gramophone was turned to its maximum volume and music echoed around the room. Women danced with one another until the men came in from the pubs. Madge was asked to dance several times and she never refused anyone. She loved dancing and it didn't matter to her what her partner looked like. By the time the Gay Gordons came, she was smiling and laughing. It turned out to be a good, fun night. Dancing around the hall and giggling with her friends, Madge planned to go dancing again, and also have trips to the cinema in the weeks to come. She realised that she could still enjoy herself, even though she had me. Life would not be as grim as she had feared.

At this point, because we had talked so much, Jessie needed a breather. The hours had flown so quickly, and it was already time for her to prepare the evening meal. She invited me to stay, but I declined. I suspected that she would want to tell Jock what she had told me. She asked me to come into the kitchen and she would tell me the rest of the story while she prepared the meal.

New Year's Eve 1941 was a solemn affair, with the war still raging in Europe. Despite blackout regulations, Annan

Council invited local residents to the town hall to see in the New Year. The street lights were switched off, or dimmed and shielded to deflect the light downward, so that they could not be seen by enemy bombers.

Jessie and Madge, along with a few other friends, walked into town to see in the New Year. Barney had not objected to this outing; Jock told him that Jessie had said someone was interested in his daughter.

At 11.45p.m., the main street in front of the town hall was overflowing with young girls, mothers with children, and those who'd been too old to go to war or were exempt from service due to their profession or job. Dressed in a dark-blue suit, a grey checked pullover, with the official chain of office dangling from his neck, Provost Dykes appeared on the balcony. It was a crisp but warm night for the time of year. Most people below in the street were wearing thick coats, scarves and gloves to keep out the cold. Those that could afford it had a half-bottle of whisky tucked into one pocket and some homemade shortbread in the other. Those who could not afford a half-bottle held onto a bottle of homemade ginger wine or a couple of screw tops they'd bought from the pub earlier.

Provost Dykes started by welcoming everyone to the celebration. He reminded those below him not to use torches irresponsibly, and not to switch on any house lights when they got home if they could be seen from the outside. These were the wartime blackout rules that could easily be forgotten after a few beers and swigs of whisky. He went on to say that the war effort was on track and "our brave sons were about to defeat the aggressors". Everyone waited with baited breath as they watched the minute hand slowly move to twelve. At precisely midnight, the bells rang out and he wished everyone below a 'Happy New Year' before making his way into the street to mingle with the crowd.

People started hugging and kissing each other and sipping from each other's half-bottles, ginger wine and beer. By 12:30a.m., most of the gathered crowd had started to make their way home along the darkened streets. Some of the young farmhands and apprentices were making their way to the river bank or park to court their girlfriends, or just have a kiss and a cuddle. After all, it was Hogmanay and a time to celebrate. At precisely 12:45a.m. on New Year's Day 1942, Madge returned to join Jessie and her friends. She was accompanied by a young farmhand called Joe Carruthers; same name, but no relation to her. Their courtship had begun.

"She looked so radiant, so happy that night," said Jessie.

I peeled the vegetables while Jessie prepared a meat pie. I asked if Mum and Dad had got married straight away. Jessie replied, "No, it was not as straightforward and easy as that."

After walking out together for a few months, Madge and Joe arranged to go for a walk around the lakes. It was a beautiful spring afternoon. As they sauntered along, Madge thought that maybe Joe was going to propose that afternoon. By five o' clock, they were sitting on the rocks where the water from the lake above them ran between the rocks, before cascading down the man-made waterfall into the second lake below. An hour earlier, Madge had finally plucked up courage and told Joe that she had an infant son. He had fallen silent and during the rest of the walk, had spoken little and seemed deep in thought. When it was time for them to part, he didn't arrange to see Madge again. She heard nothing from him for a long time.

Two months later, Joe sent a note asking Madge to meet him that Saturday at 3:00p.m. Joe seemed happy to see her as he parked his bike in the nearby woodland. They walked all the way to Powfoot, using the left-hand path, and returned using the right-hand path.

Madge told Jessie that they hadn't talked much. Joe had asked her if she had been going out and Madge had replied, "Not much."

Joe said, "I miss you and want us to get married, if you want to."

Apparently, Madge had thought her troubles were almost over, that I would have a father. Then Joe had said, "If we get married I will get a tied cottage in the village."

Without hesitation, Madge had asked, "If we get married, what about Drew?"

Joe replied, "That'll be up to you and your family."

"What do you mean, it's up to me and my family?"

His answer was, "Drew is your son and I don't want anything to do with him. You can have him adopted, or have him taken care of at the cottages, but he will not be living with us."

They had then walked silently back to the main road where Joe had left his bike. He told Madge that he would see her again the following Saturday at 3:00p.m. "You can give me your answer then," were his parting words.

With that he straddled his bike and cycled off in the direction of Annan.

******

At this point, Jock returned from the garden and Jessie made more tea while he got washed. As Jock sat down with his drink, he asked Jessie if she had finished telling me about my father.

Jessie recapped what she had told me and Jock listened intently. When Jessie got to the dancing part, Jock smiled and said, "Yes, they were a pair of beauties."

Jessie said she was just about to tell me about the night Barney agreed I should live with him after my mother got married. Jock laughed and said, "Let me tell you about what happened in the pub first while Jessie finishes the dinner."

He went on, "As you know, the nearest pub is Powfoot. The back bar on Saturday nights is always busy with farmers, farmhands, railway workers, retired locals, and back then, people exempt from service and some army people. Barney, Tom Miller and I went most Saturday nights, while Jessie and your mother sat and chatted until we came home."

As I sat there I visualised the back bar, which I knew very well. Why would a young boy be familiar with the inside of a pub? From about the age of ten, I had collected beer bottles and returned them to the pub by the back door, passing the wooden tables and bench seats to the serving hatch. There, I received one penny for each returned bottle. I recalled making a decent amount of money for my efforts.

Jock continued, "On the night in question, we'd been knocking back the screw tops and discussing when the war was likely to finish. Suddenly, Tom Miller butted into our conversation complaining that our cigarette and pipe smoke was staining the walls and making them dirty."

Jock paused to light a Woodbine. "So, I got to my feet and yelled through the smoke and noise that I thought the walls were fine, and that they shouldn't be painted again until the enemy was defeated and the war was over. Everyone cheered and yelled 'what a good idea, Jock'."

Unanimously, it was agreed that the room would not be painted or changed in any way until the war was well and truly over.

I knew this story was true because this incident had been broadcast around the village. In fact, it was several years after the war had ended before any modifications were done to the back bar.

The dinner finally cooking, Jessie re-joined us while Jock continued his story. "When we arrived back from the pub, Jessie and your mother had prepared sandwiches and tea. I suspected that something important had happened that day. I could tell that Jesse and Madge were keeping a secret until they felt it was the right time to talk. I kept quiet. After eating and drinking more beer, your mother told your grandfather that Joe wanted to marry her,"

I tried to picture what everyone might have been thinking when my mother said those words. I listened intently to Jock's words, "Your mother told your grandfather that she would marry Joe, even though he had refused to take you into his marital home. She explained that Joe suggested you could live with your grandfather, be put up for adoption, or go into a home."

I was shocked by this revelation and thought that my

father was a horrible man to treat my mother and me in this way.

"Your mum expected your grandfather to go crazy about this plan, but he didn't. Instead he lit his pipe and, looking at your mum, he said, 'go ahead and marry him. Drew can live here'."

Jessie interrupted, "Two months later, your mum and Joe were married at the Manse, because Reverend Cowie refused to marry your mother in the church."

Jock finished the story by saying, "Now what about some tea, are you staying?"

I felt a great wave of relief come over me. I stood up and gave Jessie a big hug and whispered in her ear, "Thanks for everything; I'd love to stay for tea."

******

After a warm, filling dinner, Jessie and Jock continued to tell me about my childhood years and the relationship between my father, my mother and my grandfather. There was one particular event that changed my grandfather's attitude towards me, but which never changed Joe's.

The first part of winter in 1947 had been very mild; however, severe weather across Europe and Scandinavia brought severe, harsh, cruel frosts and snow, which lasted two months. Many villages were cut off and isolated. Tractors with trailers were used to transport villagers into town to get supplies. As the weather let up and the snow started to lessen, I wanted to go outside to build a snowman. My grandfather never objected to me playing outside. It was what children were encouraged to do to keep them healthy.

Like most children I wore clogs, as they were cheap and could easily be replaced without straining the family's budget too much when they wore out. I remembered that Tommy Fergusson, the village blacksmith, was good at making clogs. First, he marked out the wooden soles and cut and carved them to suit my feet. Once this was done, he fixed the leather upper and made the holes so that I could lace them up just like boots. Then U-shaped pieces of metal, called caulkers, were nailed around the wooden soles. During the winter months, caulkers were better than rubber soles as they acted like steel skates when sliding on ice or packed and polished snow.

With caulkers I could skate across the frozen pond, which had formed in the field below Church Walk. Normally, one of my mother's two brothers would take me skating, but this time they were not around, and I thought I was big enough to go on my own. I never considered the danger; I wasn't worried that I was alone. Like any youngster, I thought I was indestructible!

After skating across the pond a few times, I became bored and decided to try another activity. I chose to go sledging down the snowy slope on Church Walk. I'd brought a tin tray that I used as a sledge. It was great fun holding on to the rim of the tray while speeding down the hill. Very soon I was soaking wet, having fallen off and rolled in the snow a few times. After an hour of dragging myself up the hill to sledge back down again, I noticed that the weather had started to change. From the look of the sky, I could see that the snow was going to start again. Grasping the tray in my hands, I headed downhill to cross the field and head home.

By the time I reached the field, the snow had started to fall heavily. I was blinded by it, and cold, icy snow ran down my neck; it made me feel sick and afraid. Searching for landmarks and seeing none, I decided to head for where I thought the road was. I guessed it was no more than a hundred yards from my current position. As the snow became more blizzard-like, I assumed the road would soon appear and I would be safe. I was cold and wet but determined, so I kept going through the soft snow looking for the road. Suddenly, there was a feeling of emptiness around me. Everything turned pitch black as if it were night-time. I lost consciousness after falling into the abyss of a six-foot snowdrift.

Jessie picked up the story. "Let me explain how you were fitting into the two households at that time. Joe was a hard worker and the marriage seemed to settle into normal family life. So far, he had treated Madge well since they had married at the Manse. Four years into the marriage and two baby girls later, Elma and Helen, Joe had relented on his decision never to allow you in his home. You spent time at the whitewashed cottage in the village. However, this was during the day; you never slept there. This change of mind had been a relief for Barney, who had been finding the situation difficult."

Even with this visiting arrangement and difficult state of affairs Barney discovered that, if things changed even more, he would really miss me. If I was allowed to join my sisters and be part of the family, he would miss the cheeky little boy, who put his work boots on and tried to walk around the kitchen making funny 'choo choo' noises when a train hurtled past no more than twenty feet from the back door.

Reluctantly, that day, because the weather had improved, he'd let me go outside to play in the snow. He'd kept his eye on the weather and saw that it was deteriorating. But now, he began to worry. He called at Jessie's house to see if I was with her. Of course, there was no sign of me. Everyone began to feel frightened and worried. Jock volunteered to help in the search. He put on his heavy railway coat, the same type Barney was wearing, opened the door and they went out to look for me. Snow whirled and twisted around them, and it was almost impossible for them to see ahead. When they could not find me around the cottages, they made their way to the bottom of the track that led to the junction of the main road and Ryhill Road, which joined Church Walk.

Battling through the blizzard, they finally reached the junction. Although I was almost obliterated by the snow, they spotted me no more than twenty feet away. I was close to the edge of a six-foot drop, between the border of the field and the road. Barney roared at the top of his voice for me to stay still, but his shouts were muffled by the snow and his words were swept away by the wind. I was almost unconscious anyway, and therefore oblivious to his orders. My body slipped and disappeared over the wall into the drift of snow that had piled against it.

Luckily, Barney and Jock were wearing their work boots, which gave them good grip in the treacherous snow. They reached the drift in seconds. Digging me out with their bare hands, it was only half a minute more before I was rescued. I was ice-cold, so Barney took off his coat and wrapped me in it. Despite the blinding snow, it took Barney only two minutes to carry my frozen body into Jock's cottage, which was warm due to the coal fire in the living room. Five minutes later, after having been stripped of my wet clothes and rubbed dry with a towel, my eyes opened. I looked up at the smiling faces and said, "Hello, Grandad, I think I must have fallen asleep. I'm hungry. What's for tea?" Barney hugged me and kissed me on the head. With a tear in his eye, he replied, "Whamel," – a term he used when we had nothing planned for tea.

From that day on, I became someone special. Someone that my grandfather adored.

CHAPTER 3

Lessons in Life

Following my narrow escape from death, my grandfather kept me close to his side. Even when he would go and sit with his friends on the old, wooden bench at the bottom of the hill, I accompanied him. I listened intently to the stories my grandfather, his friend Jock, and some of the men talked about as they sat on that old seat, smoking their pipes and Woodbine cigarettes.

Just after my rescue from the snowdrift, I learned that my uncle Jim had been taken into hospital with tuberculosis. He never recovered, and once again my grandfather's heart was broken. It was tough on everyone, but life, with all its ups and downs, had to go on.

I learned why we were going through such hard times, why we ate so much rabbit, and why my grandfather was worried about his job and paying the bills. Thousands of servicemen had returned from the war and jobs had to be found for them. The production of war materials was now unnecessary; industries' merchandise needed to change. New goods and products were required for export, to help pay for the war.

The problem was, Britain was bankrupt. The banks could not support industry; they could not loan companies the necessary funds to modernise and to install the new machinery they needed. The country was in turmoil. Women were expected to stand aside and let the returning soldiers take their jobs, but many were reluctant to give up their independence and their salaries. By the winter of 1947, the year I nearly died, Britain was suffering the worst economic crisis it had been in for a hundred years. There were fuel and gas shortages. There was a lack of housing and jobs. Scarcity of food led to increased food rationing and a thriving black market. One of the coldest seasons on record added to these issues and unemployment reached 2.3 million. Despite the country's problems, people stuck together, helped each other, and supported the government.

As the Second World War ended in 1945 new dangers emerged. Nuclear bombs were being developed and a state of tension built up between the democracies of the Western world and the communist countries of Eastern Europe. Many young men, including my uncle Alex, thought that another war was inevitable and they volunteered to join the army. Joining the army was one way of getting a job. My grandfather took it hard when Uncle Alex left for Edinburgh to join the King's Own Scottish Borderers.

Throughout this period of uncertainty, I was oblivious to the outside influences and worries that disturbed the adults in my life. I was too busy learning about my home environment. I became an expert in the life of the countryside, with all its benefits – legal and illegal. My grandfather was a poacher. I say poacher, but not big time stuff like pheasant or deer. It was just rabbit poaching.

The gamekeeper never stopped people poaching, because rabbits were a pest to the local farmers. He knew that my grandfather never used open traps, which were considered cruel. We had two ferrets, Snowy and Brownie. Snowy, my favourite, was an albino with pink eyes, whereas Brownie was light brown with grey eyes. I loved going out ferreting. I learned how to place the nets over the entrances to the burrows before sending Snowy and Brownie down the right holes to flush out the rabbits. Once chased from their burrows and after becoming entangled in the nets, you then had to kill them. This was easy. You had to hold the rabbit by its legs and, at the right moment - when its body was straight - give it a single chop to the back of its neck. That was enough to finish it off. We'd sell any spare rabbits to a local butcher.

******

By the time I was ten years old, I knew every road and path between the laird's mansion at Kinmount and the beach at Powfoot. The grounds surrounding Kinmount House were beautiful. Every year a fete was held there and the gardens opened up to the public. It was free to go to the fete, but you had to pay 6d to enter the gardens. One year I tried to sneak in for free by taking a short cut along one of the stony avenues. Unfortunately, the laird came along and stopped his big car - decorated with the bull horns fixed to the front of the bonnet, -right next to me. I recognised Captain Brook right away. I knew he did not like adults trespassing, but usually, he never seemed to mind me. As he wound down the window, he asked if I was going to the fete and gardens. I replied, "Yes, Sir."

"Good, "he said, "I will take your sixpence now."

I handed over my sixpence thinking, "That was stupid of me to get caught." I had no intention of paying sixpence to see plants and trees.

I continued to the fete feeling a bit down because now I had no money to spend. When I arrived, I could see the laird talking to a group of ladies who I recognised as being members of the Women's Rural Institute, the WRI. The laird gave me a smile and, a few minutes later, came over to talk to me. After discussing fishing and rabbiting, he asked me to hold out my hand, which I did. I felt like I was back in school and was going to get the 'taws', a leather strap with two tails on it. Instead, he placed my sixpence back in my hand and said, "That is for ice cream. No sneaking in next year."

He smiled and walked off in the direction of the big house. I stared at the shiny sixpence in my hand and a big grin spread across my face. Licking my lips, I raced off in the direction of the ice cream van.

The laird, my ice cream benefactor, had bought Kinmount House and the estate from the 8th Marquess of Queensberry, the person who, in 1867, had devised the Queensberry Rules of Boxing. The Douglas family's mausoleum at Cummertrees' old Kirk cemetery was the traditional burial place of the Marquises of Queensberry.

From a young age, the mausoleum was my castle, and the place where I would climb to the top of the walls, pretending that I was defending the village from pirates and invaders sailing up the Solway Firth. I believed that pirates invaded Cummertrees, because there are a number of gravestones in the churchyard with the skull and crossbones carved on them.

I used to read the memorial plaques that were fixed to one of the walls inside the mausoleum. My favourite one was that dedicated to Lord Francis Douglas, the son of Archibald William Douglas, 8th Marquis of Queensberry. He, along with two others, were killed on the descent of the Matterhorn, after being the first mountaineers to climb this treacherous mountain in the Swiss Alps.

All this history had happened before, and during, my childhood. At the turn of the century, Cummertrees and Powfoot expanded when Edward Brook planned a massive development programme. He wanted to create a vast seaside resort between the two. The scheme was never completed, but some of the houses were eventually built and Queensberry Terrace became part of Cummertrees village.

The terraced row comprises of fifteen three-storey, red-brick houses that boast six bedrooms, a reception area, living rooms and an indoor bath and toilet. The imposing houses overlook the fields with a view to the public right of way called Church Walk, and beyond to the Solway Firth. On Sundays, when I was a boy, people from Powfoot followed the Church Walk across the fields to attend church services at Cummertrees. The terrace, with its high-quality houses, attracted business people and middle-class workers. They were beyond the pocket of farm workers like my father.

My family lived in the older part of the village, which was

made up of a smallholding and a row of twenty-seven cottages built for the workers on the estate. My dad was one of those workers. Their whitewashed cottages were built from rubble and lime mortar. They were fitted with electric lights, but had no plumbing for running water inside the house. Water was collected in buckets from a tap situated on the old church's cemetery wall at the other end of the cottages. Heating for hot water, to wash, cook and warm the cold damp cottages, came from a coal fire in the living room. Coal sheds were at the rear of the cottages, alongside a dry lavatory, which people referred to as a 'Thunder Box'. Some gardens had a greenhouse, chickens, or both. My mother fed our chickens and collected the eggs, but always went missing when my father laid a chicken on a wooden log and chopped off its head.

As part of Edward Brook's development programme, a large pond was excavated to form a lake, which was filled with water from a stream called Glen Burn. A man-made waterfall was constructed so that the water flowed down into two smaller lakes that had been dug out. The water then flowed around two man-made islands into the Pow Burn and onwards into the Solway Firth. It was a development of approximately ten hectares in area, which was landscaped and planted with rhododendrons and a variety of shrubs, trees and plants to create a beauty spot, perfect for picnics and a pleasant walk between the two villages.

In summer, the ripening tomatoes in the village greenhouses, coupled with the strong sweet smell of the rhododendrons from the lakeside, overpowered the not-so-pleasant smells from the gardens, the thunder box, and the old church cemetery - situated just above and between the lake and the start of the whitewashed cottages. The railway cottages, where I was born, are positioned between Queensberry Terrace and the whitewashed cottages that make up the old part of the village.

Villagers from Cummertrees were envious of Powfoot, as its inhabitants benefitted more from the development and the improvements than they did. Before the changes, Cummertrees and Powfoot were very similar, as they both consisted of a single row of whitewashed cottages. As part of the development programme, Powfoot gained extra houses – fifty or more – a bowling green, a tennis court, and an eighteen-hole golf course.

All this was the area of my childhood haunts. I considered my special territory to be from Kinmount to the beach, a distance of around three miles. My other domain and stomping ground was the two miles either side of Cummertrees village. There, the lakes and surrounding woods were my favourite place for adventure, fishing, rabbiting and collecting birds' eggs. Children were lucky, as the laird didn't mind kids fishing in the lakes. Also, the farmers did not object to the collecting of birds' eggs any more than rabbiting, as both species destroyed their crops.

By the time I was ten years old, I was setting my own snares. I was careful to abide by the country rules and keep in the farmers' good books, so I never crossed fields that were newly planted with seed or walked through one where a bull was lurking. I always followed my grandfather's advice.

CHAPTER 4

The Olympian

In Cummertrees, we heard of an amazing event that was to take place in London. After a break of twelve years, due to the war, the Olympic Games were reinstated. In the summer of 1948, the Olympic Games came to London. A record number of fifty-nine nations took part with an unprecedented number of athletes coming from Britain, France and the United States. The Soviet Union was invited, but they chose not to send any athletes. They didn't want to lose more races and win fewer medals than the United States. They feared that some athletes might defect to the west. Germany and Japan, both under allied military occupation, were not allowed to send athletes to the Games.

The Olympic Games, in one respect, reflected life in our village. They also suffered from the hard times brought on after the war. At the time of the Games, food and petrol rationing was still in place. Building was difficult, too, as it was hard to get materials and skilled workmen. Because of this, the 1948 Olympics came to be known as the 'Austerity Games'.

Like dockers and miners, athletes were given increased rations. They received enough food to deliver the 5,467 calories a day essential for their sport, instead of the normal 2,600. No new venues were built for the Games and athletes were housed in existing accommodation.

My grandfather and I spent hours listening to the events on the wireless. I was interested in all sport and the Games fired my imagination and enthusiasm. The Games were the first to be shown on television, but few people were able to watch them because very few owned a television. On the beach and in the woods, I imagined I was an athlete racing to gold.

When the Games were over, Tom Miller organised competitions for the children, to see who was the 'Parish Olympic Champion'. I practised and trained and had to take on the children from my village as well as others who came from surrounding farms and estate cottages.

As I stood at the starting line, in my black plimsolls and everyday clothes, I listened carefully for the starter's words and zoomed away, seconds ahead of everyone else. With ease, I sailed through the finishing tape. I had won the hundred yards! This success was followed by a first in the high jump and second place in the long jump. To crown it all, I was declared Olympic Champion for the under-tens. My prize was a multi-coloured, hard sponge, bouncy ball. This was amazing to me, as it was something I had always wanted.

With my new piece of equipment, I practised hard every day. I threw the ball hard against a wall then I would jump and leap to catch it. Why? I wanted to be a famous goalkeeper.

******

Cummertrees Primary School was built in 1905. It was expected that the population would increase because of Edward Brook's development plans. I clearly remember my school days there. Almost everyone walked to school. There was a bus that ran every hour but walking to school was expected. Money was needed for life's necessities, not luxury travel. Some children had more difficult journeys across fields; good weather or bad, we were expected to be at school at 9:00a.m. on the dot. The school day ended at 4:00p.m. It was then that I regained my freedom. Adverse weather was no excuse for non-attendance. There were two classrooms with between twenty and thirty pupils in each class. The age range in these two seats of learning was from five to eleven years old. The schoolmaster, David McLean, didn't have to travel to work. He lived next to the school in the headmaster's house. Miss Fleming - who taught arithmetic, reading and writing - travelled every day from Annan on her bicycle.

The headmaster was a tall, slim man who wore glasses on his bald head. He was very strict, but I liked him because he let us play football at break time. At first, I had a slate for all my written work. My mistakes were easily corrected with a damp rag and a small tin containing water. We learned by repetition and I can still recite my times-tables and spelling words, like Mississippi, without any trouble. The best part of learning, and my favourite lesson, involved practical skills. Mr McLean took the boys into the garden and showed us how to dig a plot and grow vegetables.

At lunchtime, we all trooped into the dining room where there were two long trestle tables and four benches. Everyone had to be quiet while we said 'grace,' in thanks for the food we were about to receive. The only meal I can remember old Mrs Frazer, the school cook, serving was tatties and runny mince, followed by sago or rice pudding with a bit of jam in it. Meals were warm and filling. There was nothing special on the school menu, another result of rationing!

The best time of the day was morning break, when we had a small bottle of milk. Milk was delivered to the school every day, in any weather. The milk froze in the bottles in winter and the cream rose to the top. The foil top was like a silver flat cap on the top of the bottle neck. In winter, the silver tops were pecked by the birds so that they could reach the cream.

The daily timetable never varied; we started with assembly followed by arithmetic, writing, spelling, gardening and games. There was no set timetable and the length of each lesson depended on how the teacher felt. In those days, everyone had to take an exam when they were 10/11 years old. Consequently, it was called the 11+ exam. The year and day when it was my turn for the exam, I had no idea what it was for. Nobody had explained the importance of this time in my life – or, more likely, I hadn't been listening or thought it wasn't important!

Most of the children were not academic in our rural community. We knew what we would do in our adult life – we'd follow the pattern of our parents' lives. Few people passed the 11+ and went onto grammar school. Almost everyone progressed into secondary school; girls ended up in domestic industry and boys would be in the technical stream.

My education out of school was in and around the farmyard and countryside. Most of the other younger boys lived in Powfoot or on the local farms. I often went to Barrasgate because that was where the Russells lived and where my dad worked. Close by was Holybush Farm, where my friend Gordon lived. On these visits, I learned about gathering in sheaves of corn and stacking them together into 'stooks' to allow the corn to dry.

I became an expert at milking cows and the less-inspiring skill of how to clean and wash out the byres. I longed for the school summer holidays, which lasted for seven weeks. This time seemed to flash by in an instant. I was outside constantly with friends or alone, helping on the farm, catching rabbits or fishing. My life was full and fun-filled outside the confines of the classroom and school routine.

My circle of friends expanded when Ian, Herman and Joyce McMinn moved from the village of Hollywood, near Dumfries, to Lake View at Powfoot. Their father had taken the job of caretaker at Powfoot Golf Club. Ian and I became instant friends, spending a lot of our time together. Fishing in the Pow Burn was our main pastime and Herman became an expert, outstripping us with his skills. He could catch trout with a fly rod, whereas Ian and I had to be satisfied with catching eels and 'skellies' - a dirty fish with lots of scales and bones. By this time, my grandfather had stopped trying to protect me; I was growing up fast and learning how to look after myself. I was eleven years old and prepared for secondary school.

Growing up in a country village, surrounded by beautiful countryside, was not without danger, as my previous dice with death in a snowdrift had proved. I was confident and sure of my strength and abilities. I eagerly swam in the dangerous currents of the Solway Firth, fished wherever I wanted in the rivers and lakes, and went rabbiting around the surrounding fields and marshes. For someone who would today still be considered a child, wildlife and animals were always a constant danger, and I was not indestructible.

My life hung in the balance once again as another adventure almost cost me my life. The two islands in the centre of the lower lakes were great places to look for treasure and pretend to be a pirate, or even a Red Indian attacking a US cavalry fort. It depended on which film was showing at the cinema on Saturday mornings as to what I pretended to be. That day, dressed in shorts, an old school shirt and plimsolls, I decided to go and look for treasure on one of the two islands. I had not been to any of the islands for some time because of the cold weather.

The sun was shining, and flowers were starting to bloom. The lakes smelled fresh. The weather had enticed me to the islands. The best way to get to them was to cross the Pow Burn that flowed around them, by stepping carefully across an old, slimy tree trunk that had blown down years before. The tree had fallen perfectly across the burn to make a natural bridge, so I could cross the water without getting wet. The area surrounding the islands was like a minefield; there were bushes, tall reeds and bulrushes, plus holes with water in them that were difficult to see.

As I headed towards my goal, I imagined that there were crocodiles hiding in the pools of water just waiting to eat me. I took out the old penknife that my grandfather had given me and cut a branch to make a sword from a nearby bush. Next, I tied and knotted a red-and-white-spotted handkerchief around my head and pulled a black patch over my left eye. I now looked like a real pirate. Progress through the reeds and bulrushes was slow, but, eventually, I would be safely on the island.

On hearing a hissing sound, I stopped and listened intently. I recognised that it was coming from a swan. A mute swan, with large, strong, arm-breaking wings! I could just see one sitting on its nest. Close by, another had opened its wings to their full span and had started to rush towards me. It towered right over me. I then screamed as its wings came crashing down, smashing into my body. The swan pushed its neck straight out and opened its wings for a second attack, which I thought would finish me off. I was going to die.

Attack or flee? I chose the latter, and turned as fast as I could, heading back to the burn. I was in pain, but not entirely sure where it was coming from. My escape route was hindered by a mixture of reeds, bulrushes and pools of water. Incredibly, and thankfully, I reached the burn just ahead of the swan. Ignoring the tree trunk, I jumped as far as I could into the burn and waded the rest of the way across. I could hear angry hissing and the whine of swan's wings behind me. Fortunately for me, the swan realised that its nest was now out of danger and gave up the chase. Sitting on the bank, shivering and shaking, and with a very sore shoulder, I decided to give up treasure-hunting, for that day at least.

When I arrived home, my grandfather asked me why I was so wet and bruised. I replied, "I fell in the burn, that's all. Can I get a sandwich? I'm starving."

Sometimes, it was better not to tell the truth. My brush with injury or death might have got me into trouble!

******

Powfoot, the nearest village to Cummertrees, was around a mile away, depending on the route taken. You could either take the long way round and pass the old quarry, or take the shortest route over the Church Walk.

The old quarry area had been turned into a quoiting pitch, which was a popular sport where local villagers met during the summer evenings to pitch their iron rings, called quoits.

These rings were rounded on one side, flat on the other and weighed 8-12 pounds. The quoits were hurled at a steel pin driven into a three-foot square clay bed 22 yards away.

Just past the quarry was the 'White Bridge', which passed over the Pow Burn. Local legend said the ghost of a young girl, who had been raped and murdered in the nearby woods, would often appear. I never saw the ghost, I'm happy to say; however, I always remembered the story and rushed past the bridge, especially at night.

The grass and vegetation around the old quarry and the lakes had always been well looked after, but after Uncle Jim passed away no one trimmed the bushes or cut the grass around the paths. The green-keeper from the golf club occasionally came to control the long grass by burning it. Whilst watching and controlling the flames, he would give us tips on how to catch trout and tell us when someone was looking for a caddie on the golf course.

You could make a bit of money as a caddie. I tried it once, as I was always on the lookout to make money, but I did not understand the game. I made a hash of the job because I couldn't hand the correct club to the golfer when he asked. Though I loved sport, golf didn't interest me at all. I couldn't be bothered to put my mind towards learning about it. It was too slow for me. I loved speed and action, so it was the first and last time I caddied.

Powfoot was popular for visitors, especially at the weekends when families would take the bus to the end of the Powfoot road and walk the half mile to the beach. On the beach itself, a swimming pool had been built for soldiers based in the area during the war to use for recreation. Because of the flat sands and continually low water level, the pool had to be situated a-hundred-and-fifty yards from the shoreline so that the water was replenished when the tide came in.

The Solway Bore came between the pool and the central channel, which made it was a very dangerous area. To add to that danger, the tide came in fast; if you were not careful you could become cut off, or worse still, bogged down in treacherous quicksand. I was quite a good swimmer, especially in salt-water. I tested my skills and bravery, and probably foolhardiness, by walking beyond the pool towards the channel where the Bore came down and the tide swept in. When I thought I'd gone far enough, I'd wait for the tide to reach my shoulders, then I'd swim back to the shoreline, riding on the crest of the waves. A foolish thing to do but the danger did not scare me.

Salmon nets were located at Powfoot and various other locations all down the coastline. They were an added interest and bonus to my friends and me for our families' food supplies. Stake nets were fixed into the sand at right angles to the shore. They covered several hundred yards and had a number of traps set into them to capture the salmon that followed the netting barriers rather than attempting to swim through them. The salmon that swam along the barrier, which is called a leader, ended up in the trap.

As the tide ebbed, the fishermen would follow it out and collect the trapped salmon. Often, flat fishes (flounders) would also be trapped; they would lay on the seabed covered in sand. Once the fishermen left, I would collect the flounders and take them home.

One time, I thought I had caught a strange fish. On picking it up, I saw that it had tentacles. I carried the creature home, unsure of what to do with it. I didn't fancy it for my own dinner, so I opened the door of the ferret hutch and told Snowy and Brownie to enjoy their treat. Days later, I was surprised to find that my grandfather was upset with me. My act of kindness had misfired. The ferrets hadn't been too well following their meal. My defence was, "But I thought ferrets liked fish."

Grandfather glared at me and growled, "Fish? That was

octopus! Never feed them stuff if you don't know what it is –
otherwise, I'll skelp your ears!"

The ferrets were his pride and joy. I'd learnt another
lesson in life.

CHAPTER 5

The Rat Catcher

The good thing about where I lived, in the railway cottages, is that they were dry inside. This was unlike the whitewashed cottages up the hill where water could be seen on the inside walls when it rained, and the air was damp for long periods. A roaring fire, which was always well stoked and supported by a paraffin heater, kept the rooms in the cottage warm and dry.

Outside it was not so pleasant. The outbuildings and the midden, where waste and ash were dumped, attracted vermin - especially rats. Brown ones. The rat is an incredibly adaptable mammal that only needs shelter and food to survive. A rat will eat pretty much anything, from fruit and seeds to human food waste, insects, birds' eggs, and even small mammals. Few rats survive longer than a year, but their prolific breeding habits mean there are never-ending colonies of them.

I had personal knowledge of this fact. Our midden was a concrete bunker, ten feet by ten feet and five-feet deep. It was shared by the three families occupying the cottages. The cottages had been built to within twenty feet of the railway banking, which meant that the buildings shook each time a train passed. The banking was perfect for rats to burrow in and make their homes, and the midden provided a continuous food supply.

Every four months my father brought a tractor with a high-sided trailer from the farm to the cottages; it was practically the only time he ever ventured there. He'd take the waste to the council tip for disposal. While the men shovelled out the waste, we three boys living at the cottages - Tommy, Phil and I, armed with spades or big sticks - would line up and block the path, to prevent rats running back from the midden to their holes in the railway bank. It was not difficult to kill a few on the day the midden was cleared. I hated rats and was not afraid of them. When the kitchen light was on, I'd often look out towards the banking and see their eyes glowing pink in the dark.

Another way we controlled rats was to burn them out. I'd roll up old newspapers, soak them in paraffin and stuff them into the rat holes before setting the paper alight. It was difficult at first to get the paper to burn, so my grandfather suggested using a bicycle pump to get more air into the holes, so that the paper would burn for longer. Once I got the right combination of paper, air and paraffin, I could make the fire last long enough to hear rats squealing, as they tried to escape from the other holes. I'd cover the exits with some of my grandfather's old rabbit nets, and those that were not burned became trapped and felled with a spade. Some must have survived by digging deeper, because they were never completely eliminated. A cruel practice, but necessary for the health of our small community.

******

Things were due to change in our house and I wondered how it might affect me. My uncle Alex had been in the army for almost two years. It was a rare occurrence and reason for celebration when he finally came home on leave. He always looked so smart in his tartan trousers and checked cap. On this particular visit, he told us he had a girlfriend in Edinburgh who he was due to marry in a few months, before he left the army. They would then come to live with us.

I was excited at the thought of my uncle coming back to live with us, but I was not sure about having a woman come and stay, forever. Since Uncle Alex had left to go to the army, my grandfather and I had coped very well. I could get my own breakfast and I got school dinners. My grandfather would cook his meal when he came in from work. If I was hungry, which I normally was, then he would cook for both of us. My grandfather could make a great rabbit stew.

What would happen with a woman in the kitchen? Would my circumstances change? There'd been a lot of upheaval in my life - was this going to be the next? I had seen very little of my mother and father. When my mother came to clean and do the washing I was usually at school, out setting my snares, or playing in the woods. I would sometimes see my father, but I never felt comfortable in his presence.

I was digging up potatoes from the garden when I spotted my uncle Alex getting off the bus. I dropped my spade and tripped over the bucket, knocking potatoes everywhere, as I stumbled across the garden and ran to the cottage.

"Uncle Alex is home and he has a woman with him," I shouted.

Work on Saturdays finished at midday, so Tom Miller and Jock McDougall were also at home. Word spread like wildfire around the three cottages. Within minutes, several adults and children appeared outside the cottages to greet the homecoming hero soldier and his new wife.

The men all shook hands and I stood in the background to wait my turn, feeling apprehensive. The lady looked just like a girl; she was not much bigger than me, with golden hair, blue eyes and freckles on her face. I was not sure if I wanted to meet her, so I waited for my grandfather to say something. Instead of introducing me, Grandad sent me inside to tidy up the living room and kitchen.

I could hear more chatter going on outside as Alex introduced Catherine to the Millers and McDougalls. My grandfather was giving instructions to everyone. Alex took their suitcase and kit bag into the living room and, once inside, he drew back the green velvet curtain that separated the recess from the living room. I was being nosey and peered through the window. He placed the suitcase and kit bag on the double bed and I heard him say, "This is our bed."

Minutes later, Jessie called out that the food was ready. It was a good spread that made my mouth water and my hands eager to grab a sandwich, cake, anything! She had prepared scones and boiled egg and spam sandwiches, which she set on the living room table. Jessie turned, smiled and said, "Welcome to the railway cottages, Catherine," and turned to leave. Catherine returned the smile and replied, "Thanks for the sandwiches and everything. They look delicious. Please call me Cathy."

All this introducing and politeness was too much for me and delaying precious eating time. My stomach rumbled and I went to help myself to a sandwich. Something, some inner thought, made me stop and hesitate. Hadn't I been told at school to be polite to ladies and to offer them my seat when the bus was full? I turned and looked sheepishly at the pretty, golden-haired young woman. Now that I had remembered my manners, I asked Catherine if I could have a sandwich.

"Yes, of course. Help yourself, you're a growing lad," she replied. "And, please, do call me Aunt Cathy."

****

Cooking, cleaning and washing for four people could have been a nightmare for this young Irish woman. She found it difficult and often frustrating, but she coped. Aunt Cathy settled in and adapted to the everyday routine of her new home.

The outbuildings consisted of a washhouse, three dry toilets, and the midden - with the drying green next to them. She became an expert at lighting the fire to boil the water to soak the clothes before scrubbing them clean. Uncle Alex's clothes, and Grandfather's, certainly needed a mighty scrub as the former worked at the munitions factory a mile away and the latter was a railway worker. Dirt, sweat, oil and grease penetrated the thick, heavy overalls and made them smell.

Fortunately, one of the perks of my grandfather's job was that he got a free supply of coal. Often, train drivers would throw a big lump of coal on to the banking as it slowed down at the bridge. Extra coal was always appreciated. The coal fire kept the cottage warm and also dried the clothes hanging on the pulley and clothes horse when it rained.

Aunt Cathy wasn't left to do everything as, after my return from school, I had plenty of chores. I washed and scraped potatoes and carrots. Every two weeks, I dug a hole along the railway banking and helped my grandfather carry the toilet bucket, as we buried the smelly contents in the deep hole.

I liked helping Cathy because she told me stories about Achill Island, Ireland, where she was born. A faraway look would come into her eyes, as if she had been transported back there. She told me that she had seven sisters and three brothers, and that life with them and her parents made it the most beautiful place in the world. It had wonderful sandy beaches that stretched for miles and miles and it was where she swam in summer with her brothers and sisters. They spent hours playing on the beach and squealing at the coldness of the water as they splashed each other. "Laughter and fun," she said, "was what happened when we got together."

At school, her teacher told her all about the history, geography and nature of Achill Island. She'd been on numerous school visits where the teachers took the pupils around the natural features of sea, cliffs and hills. They visited historical sites and buildings and watched and studied the animals and plants that filled Aunt Cathy's 'Eden', for that was what her birthplace was to her. It was her little piece of paradise.

One of her tales was about the pirate queen, Grace O'Malley, a famous person in the island's history. She was the daughter of a Gaelic chieftain, who excelled as a seafarer and pirate. Songs were written about her exploits, which local people sang when they gathered around the warm fire in the pub on a cold or wet night.

Aunt Cathy told me about her favourite haunt, the most famous place on the whole island: the 'deserted village'. These are small, circular, single-roomed dwellings with a hole in the ceiling to let out smoke. People did not live in these houses permanently; they had to move cattle around the county to give them decent grazing and lived in different locations during the summer and winter periods. The cottages have now been abandoned, except for the sheep that graze the land. Achill is famous for its mutton.

I asked, "If it's so beautiful, why did you leave?"

Cathy smiled and explained, "Well you see, it is the most beautiful place in the world, but most of the time, it is raining or foggy, so you can't see it. And winter, brrrrrrr! It's so cold and there's only peat to burn. So cold, you have to sleep in your clothes."

She paused and pulled her cardigan closely around her, as if she could feel the freezing temperature of those days. Her glazed eyes showed that she was recalling more of her past. "When I left school there were no jobs. Many men left the island to go to Scotland where they could find work in the fields. Villages would empty. Without the men, the fun and laughter disappeared." She chuckled, "No dances, so there was little chance of finding a husband!" She sighed and looked sad, then added, "When you have to live in a very small house, with no prospects for the future, you do what you have to do … you leave."

******

Life at the railway cottages soon developed a strict routine. Cathy had to travel by bus into Annan twice a week to buy meat and other essentials. This was the era before the refrigerator, so food had to be bought daily, or regularly at least. The milkman, practically extinct in the twenty-first century, came daily, and the butcher's van came once a week. On her trips into town, and despite rationing, she still managed to bring me a toffee chew or gobstopper as a treat.

Aunt Cathy and I became close. I loved her stories and the songs she sang. This closeness, and my growing love for her, meant that I would do anything to help her. I volunteered to do jobs around the house and would risk being late for school. I'd catch the 7:50a.m. bus into town and dash to do the shopping at the butchers or nip to Isherwood's for some bread and cold meat, just so she could spend a day at home. It broke the routine of her hard-working life and gave her some time - if not to relax, to at least to do things more slowly.

Life for me was good, though I saw less of my mother. She was pregnant again and was busy looking after my three sisters. Joe, who I thought was my father, never came to see how things were at the railway cottages. I thought this was a bit strange, but assumed that he was far too busy with his job and the extra work of renovating the cottage they'd recently been allocated. Number Fourteen was bigger than Number Eleven and it had the bonus of an extra room and a kitchen extension. There'd be more space, which made me wonder if I could move back in with my sisters. This hope flashed into my head when I heard the news.

Once Aunt Cathy arrived, I really enjoyed Christmas. On my first Christmas with her, I sent a letter up the chimney to Santa and hung up my sock. Despite rationing, my sock was full of goodies. I got the 'Dandy' comic annual that had been top of my list.

Within weeks of this happy Christmas, the tide started to turn. We were all at home; Cathy had made a pot of tea and was just fetching in some treacle scones when Grandad's left arm dropped to the side of the chair. He tried to talk, but could not speak. Cathy, sensing something was seriously wrong, ran outside and straight up the hill to the village telephone box. She dialled 999 and an hour later Grandad was in Dumfries Infirmary. He'd suffered a stroke. From then on, he needed help to shave and dress; many other actions that we take for granted now proved impossible for him to do alone. What was I going to do without my grandad? What would happen to me, if the worst thing happened and he was no longer there to look after me? I tried to do what I could to help my grandfather and Aunt Cathy. I could see that she was overworked, and that not having any of her own family around her was making her unhappy.

One night, I overheard her telling Uncle Alex that she was pregnant and that they would need a house of their own.

When she told me her good news I was pleased and said, "I hope you have a little boy."

My hope for a boy was not to be. Cathy's first child was a daughter named Teresa, who was born in June 1952. The pregnancy had taken its toll on the family and Cathy found it difficult to cope with my grandfather as well as looking after a new baby.

Her breaking point came the following winter, on a freezing, cold morning, just before Alex got home from his night shift.

I was getting dressed so I could catch the bus and go shopping when I heard screams. I threw the bedroom door open just in time to see a giant brown rat jump down from the Silver Cross pram, fly across the floor and squeeze under the tallboy that stood against the opposite wall. Still screaming, and holding the shovel in one hand and the poker in the other, Cathy headed for the heavy tallboy. She pushed her shoulder against the unit and heaved. The tallboy slid on the floor and the rat made its way out from underneath. In a single movement, Cathy felled the rat with the poker, then scooped it up with the coal shovel and threw it on the burning fire. Afterwards, she collapsed on the floor. I ran to comfort her until Uncle Alex arrived home.

"Something has to happen, has to change. I can't go on like this," she sobbed to her husband as he came through the door.

CHAPTER 6

The Death

Every family is prone to good and bad luck. Before Teresa was born a famous family, far away from where I lived, suffered its own tragedy. On Wednesday 6th February 1952, when I got home from school, my grandfather told me that King George VI had died, and that Princess Elizabeth was to be our new queen. School subsequently gave us the day off to mourn the death of the king. Grandad said that I had to show respect, and that I was not to set my snares or go fishing that day. I was to stay in the house and listen to the wireless. I was a bit stunned by his attitude. This was the first time my grandad had ever mentioned a king. He shook his head and sighed saying, "Let's hope that this will be the end of sadness this year."

I was outside when I saw my mother approach the cottages. I ran to meet her and give her a hug. When I went to put my arms around her she held up her hands and said, "Drew, I don't feel well." She looked pale and her face was drawn, so instead of hugging her I walked with her to the house. When we got inside, Aunt Cathy said, "Drew, put the kettle on and make your mum some tea. And put lots of sugar in it."

I did as I was told and went to the kitchen. From there I could hear everyone talking. I overheard my mother telling Grandad that she was pregnant and she could be having twins. I called from the kitchen, "I want a brother, but one of each will be okay."

I was happy with her news, but Mum seemed very worried and not very well. She told Grandad that she was really concerned about her health. She'd given birth to four healthy children, but unfortunately, her last pregnancy with twins was a sad event. They died just hours after they were born. She thought that her body would not cope with another pregnancy, particularly if it was twins. Her morning sickness and the hard work of raising three girls was not helping her to cope. Listening at the door, I felt scared. Grandad was not in good health and now my mother could be in danger.

By mid-July my mother stopped coming to visit us, as she was experiencing more nausea and pain. Doctor Dudgeon came to check her over and could not find anything wrong with the pregnancy. He tried to reassure her, but she would not be appeased. On 21st August, Mum was rushed to Dumfries Infirmary in great pain. She died the next morning after haemorrhaging. She was twenty-eight years old.

******

I could not understand why my mother had left my grandfather and me. I was angry because I did not know what to do.

Three days later, Uncle Alex told me that we had to go and say goodbye to Mum. When we set off to walk up the hill the sun was shining and I felt hot. When we arrived at number 14 my father came out to meet us. He shook hands with everyone except me. He asked us if we wanted to go into the bedroom together or separately. My grandfather said that he would take me in and let Alex and Cathy go ahead of us. They made their way into the bedroom to say their goodbyes.

A few minutes later, instinctively, I took my grandfather's hand and followed him into the bedroom. I knew what a coffin was, but this was the first time I had seen a dead person. The shiny, oak coffin with gleaming brass handles rested on a stand next to the bed. The lid half covered the coffin and there lay my mum. She was wearing her favourite blue dress. I gasped at the sight of her. I was amazed at how young and beautiful she looked. I spoke my thoughts aloud to my grandfather and he agreed. We stayed a while just looking at her. Grandad squeezed my hand, "It's time to say goodbye to your mum." He bent over the coffin and put his hand on Mum's head then kissed her on the cheek. Following his lead, because I didn't know what to do, I did exactly the same. At the door I turned and said, "Bye, Mum," then I started to sob.

Mum's funeral was on a Wednesday, six days after she passed away. It was a warm day with little cloud in the sky, as we all walked up the hill to the old Kirk. I could tell that Grandad did not feel comfortable as we entered the church. I took his hand and helped him to the front pew where my father was already sitting alongside four of my uncles and aunts. We joined them and the rest of my uncles, aunts and cousins occupied the other pews near the front. The church was full; however, my sisters were nowhere to be seen.

Reverend Cowie, who had worked in the parish for as long as I could remember, stood behind the pulpit. I liked Reverend Cowie because he made Sunday School interesting and he told funny stories. The service did not take long, and when it came to the Lord's Prayer I knew that it was over. I had learned the Lord's Prayer at Sunday School; Reverend Cowie had told me it was the last prayer said at a church service.

Moments later, two men wearing long black coats and bowler hats came in and stood beside my mother's coffin. The people who had carried the coffin in came forward and, placing the coffin once again on their shoulders, carried it outside to the waiting hearse. Holding my grandfather's hand, I followed the coffin out to where John Dalrymple's big Humber Hawk taxi was waiting behind the hearse.

As I climbed in, I was surprised to see that none of my aunts were in the car. When we set off to follow the hearse to the cemetery, which was only a quarter of a mile away, I looked for my Aunt Cathy and Aunt Bella, but could not see them anywhere. All I could see were the men in their black suits, white shirts and black ties. I asked Uncle Alex, "Where are Aunt Cathy and Aunt Bella?"

Before he could answer, my grandfather replied, "Women

and children don't attend the service at the cemetery. You are your mum's oldest son so you must attend."

When we approached the grave, my father moved to the head of my mother's coffin and picked up the cord lying on the coffin lid. My grandad handed me the cord at my mother's feet and he held the cord next to me. My uncles picked up the other cords.

During the short service, the rope felt wet and cold in my hands and tears started to roll down my cheeks. I grasped the rope until my knuckles were white, holding firmly onto the mum I did not want to lose to this deep, dark hole. As we took the weight of the coffin, the supporting boards were pulled away until I felt the full weight of the coffin in my hands. It was so light! I glanced around to look at the faces of my relatives and saw tears glistening in their eyes. Slowly and gently, we lowered the coffin down. I will always remember that moment.

When the service concluded, my grandfather led me out of the cemetery gate where John Dalrymple and his car were waiting. Grandad said, "John, I'll walk back with Drew and Alex." Determinedly, he set off to walk back to the railway cottages with Alex and me following.

Once there, the door was opened to reveal sandwiches, scones, lemonade and bottles of beer. This was the 'wake' meal. Our neighbours were either already there or they followed us in. I looked around the room for a sign of my father and my relatives. I kept expecting them to arrive. No one appeared. I did not see my father, my sisters or any of my relatives again that day. This puzzled and upset me. Were they having their own wake somewhere else? Why? I guessed it was because my grandfather and Uncle Alex didn't get on very well with my father and some of my relatives.

******

A month after my mother died, I started a new school. My primary school years had ended and I now attended Annan Academy Secondary School. I had little interest in academic subjects; my only passion was for the sports section that had opened up to me. I trained whenever I could and Bert Lorraine, my PE teacher, soon recognised my sporting skills. Very quickly, I became the school team's goalkeeper.

My father had found this summer particularly hard, as his wife had just passed away and he was not coping with the tragedy. When I went to visit my sisters, or to the farm to play with my friends, he acknowledged me but that was all. Did I remind him too much of his wife and the gap she had left in his life?

1953 came quickly, but there was little celebration at Christmas or New Year. This year would be a year marked with epic achievements, national and local. We would have a new monarch because it was coronation year. All around Great Britain, people would be celebrating the crowning of a new queen: Queen Elizabeth II.

Even though rationing was still in force and special treats were scarce, folks scrimped, searched and somehow found food, bunting, banners and booze. It was a national holiday, so along with the rest of Great Britain, I enjoyed the day off school on 2nd June. There were celebrations all over the country: street parties, galas, travelling fairs. I won vouchers at the games held in the school grounds, which I exchanged for money at Toni's Cafe. Even the weather seemed to be celebrating that day, as the sun shone down on the new queen's subjects. It was an excellent day, which concluded with a huge bonfire on the hill at Repentance Tower. There, with the crowds of happy, smiling folks, I watched fireworks, scoffed sandwiches and drank lemonade. What a celebration!

Life was not happy and carefree after that occasion. I could see that my father was struggling bringing up my three sisters. I convinced myself that the pressure of having three young girls to bring up without a mother to care for them was why he ignored me. I never thought that maybe he was wiping me out of his memory and life. I felt sorry for my father.

One day I met my sister, Elma, and she told me that the

whole family was going away for the summer holidays to stay with our Uncle Dode and Aunt Annie in Seaton Sluice. I was a little jealous of this treat and wondered why I'd been excluded. I was part of this family, wasn't I?

I thought about them a lot during their absence, wondering what they would be doing on the beaches in Northumberland, jealous of the ice cream and treats they were probably consuming. However, during their holiday, my grandfather suffered another stroke. I was therefore glad that I'd been left at home, to help look after him.

To make things worse, Aunt Cathy received a letter confirming that she and Uncle Alex had been allocated one of the newly-built council houses - but not in Annan, it was in Newbie, one of the villages around two miles from our town.

I listened in to the discussions whenever I could, wondering where I would fit into all these changes. Fortunately, Barbara, a close friend of my mum's, urgently needed a place to live and the matter was settled quickly. Matt and Barbara, and their three children, moved into our cottage, and Alex, Cathy and Teresa moved into a new two-bedroomed council house in Newbie. Thankfully, I got to stay in the house I knew with the grandfather I loved.

Everyone seemed pleased and I enjoyed having other children around me; however, Grandad was unhappy. He was not used to so many children, and he felt as if he was losing control of his home and his life.

******

The situation eventually became difficult for everyone and Aunt Bella stepped in to help. She went to the council and was told that our lodgers would be allocated a council house within a few months. In the meantime, if Grandad moved in with her he would be deemed a priority for an old person's bungalow in Annan, as her house would be classed as being overcrowded.

Aunt Bella told Grandad that I could share his room. I could not go and live with my father as he would not allow me to live with him. His excuse was that he was finding it hard looking after three girls by himself and could not cope with another child. Two weeks later, we moved to Annan to live with Aunt Bella, her husband and five children in a two-roomed cottage. At this point I felt and believed the stories I had heard over the years, that I truly was the 'bastard' unwanted child.

This single-bedroom cottage on Scott's Street was now my home and I spent as little time as possible there. I could see that this made my grandfather unhappy, but there was very little that I could do to comfort him in the cramped living conditions. He had his old wireless, which was on from the time he woke up until he fell asleep again. I just learnt how to survive in this new environment.

Aunt Bella managed the situation in her home as best as she could. Grandad and I shared the only bedroom, which meant that Bella, her husband Robert, and their five children shared the living room. With no running water, an outside toilet and only basic cooking facilities, life was difficult.

I decided that I needed to work to get money for my own necessities, so that I would not be a burden on this family who had taken me into their home. Working also meant that I would not get in the way as I'd be out of the house. It was easy to get a job delivering milk as the start time for this was 5:00a.m. It really wasn't necessary for me to earn money as Grandad was paying Bella for our food and clothing, so she let me keep any money that I earned.

I was busy and did not give much thought to my living situation, or what would happen to me if, or rather when, my grandfather moved into a pensioner's bungalow. I assumed so much. I thought I would move in with him and we'd continue to look after one another.

Months passed and there was no sign of a pensioner's bungalow and the lodgers were still living at the cottage. My grandfather's health deteriorated and he seldom left the bedroom. Aunt Bella took him his food and looked after him as best she could. Meanwhile, I was left to do more or less what I wished, so I spent my time roaming the streets with my friends and playing football.

At weekends, probably because I felt claustrophobic in Aunt Bella's house, I walked to the railway cottages and had my tea with Jessie and Jock. They always seemed pleased to see me and kept me up to date with everything that was happening in the village. I saw my sisters when I was there. I could tell from watching and listening to what they said that my father was finding it difficult to manage his work life as well as raising three girls.

******

Almost two years after Mum's death, my father continued to find it difficult to cope. He'd arranged for old Mrs Ferguson to come each day. She arrived after Elma, my eldest sister, had already got her siblings washed and fed before getting herself ready for school. Mrs Ferguson looked after Helen and Ann until Elma returned from school. Elma then took over until my father got in from work. Elma had to do more for the family than my father wanted.

Harvest was coming up and, even with the help of neighbours, he knew that he could not deal with the increased workload. Also, Elma would have to be a mother to her sisters during the long hours he would be absent from home during harvesting time. He had to find a solution that would benefit both him and Elma. Consequently, when school closed in June for the long summer break, my father boarded a train in Annan and headed for Newcastle. He was not alone; his three girls accompanied him. They boarded a bus for Seaton Sluice after the steam train journey. Aunt Annie had once more volunteered to take care of the girls during the summer holidays.

By the time he returned home, my father had realised that he required a permanent solution that would alleviate the situation for both himself and Elma. He did the only thing that was open to him: he advertised for a wife.

Word spread quickly and within two weeks, two

potential wives visited his cottage. They were set a test to find out whether they'd be suitable. On separate evenings, they had to bake scones and cakes for my father and my two sisters. Marilyn White was the first lady to come and bake. Jessie had told me when the baking trial was taking place and on that night I made sure that I was there. Marilyn was quite a jolly person, humming while she baked and asking questions about the school and people in the village. I liked her and thought that her cakes and scones were the best I had ever tasted. She left on the last bus, not knowing if she was going to become a bride.

The following week Elizabeth McLean arrived on her pushbike. I did not see her bake nor did I taste the scones and cakes she made; maybe I was playing football or doing one of my money-making jobs. Her baking must have been the best because, after a short courtship, my father and Lizzie, as my father called her, married at the Manse on 20th November, just a month before Christmas. My sisters had a new mother. Would she be my mother, too? Time would tell. The first few months of the following year would bring change.

CHAPTER 7

A New Mother and a New Home

The big freeze of February 1955 resulted in great hardship across Britain. Roads were blocked with snow, and up to thirty-thousand people across Britain died that year. My family suffered, too, as my grandfather developed pneumonia and was admitted to Dumfries Infirmary. When his illness was under control, he was moved to Newbie to live with Aunt Cathy and Uncle Alex. I was to stay at Aunt Bella's until a more permanent solution could be found.

The next two weeks were the worst of my life. I had lost Mum and Grandad was no longer with me, due to his move to Newbie. When I stopped crying and came to my senses, I realised that I might be homeless before long. I had the only bedroom and Bella's daughters were growing up fast. Aunt Bella would soon need the bedroom. I had been allowed to come to live with Grandad so that he would have company. I couldn't see Aunt Bella's husband wanting me to live with them for much longer.

My first thoughts were to ask Aunt Cathy and Uncle Alex if I could live with them. It was not right that I should ask them. When I had visited previously I could see that they were happy in their new home. The only spare bedroom was Teresa's, and this was now needed for Grandad, and possibly Cathy's family when they visited. I heard myself talking out loud, "Besides, who wants to live in Newbie? I don't have any friends there; it'd be a horrible place to live." I put the thoughts of going to Newbie out of my mind.

A children's home was never a consideration. I feared and hated the idea of rules and regulations governing my life. I knew two boys who lived in one and had heard stories of the things they had to endure. I decided that I only had one choice. I was going to confront my father - if he was my father, which I doubted.

I had never asked my father for anything important. I knew that I would need to be careful, with regards to how I'd ask if I could come and live with him and my three sisters. I decided on a plan of action. The next day was a Sunday, a more leisurely day. The best time to call in would be around 3:00p.m., midway between dinner and tea, when everyone was relaxed after a good Sunday lunch. If I was lucky and successful in my plan, I might even be asked to stay for tea.

Next day I kept repeating the script I'd prepared in my head. To keep my nerves under control, I played football in the morning with my mates in the park. I tied my football boot-laces together and slung the boots around my shoulders. I didn't have any smart clothes to change into so that I could make a good impression. I only possessed my school uniform, my football gear, and some old school clothes, which were now relegated to 'playing out' clothes. I put my plimsolls on over my football socks and headed off to sort out my future. What an unruly picture I must have made with my tousled hair, mud-smeared Academy School football shirt and torn school trousers.

It took just forty minutes to walk from the park to Cummertrees. Queensberry Terrace was almost deserted as I walked towards what I hoped would be my future home. Mrs Quinn, at number 15, was outside looking for her cat. I stopped to say hello and told her that I hoped to bring her a rabbit soon, as I was coming back to the village to live. Was this a presumptuous hope?

I climbed the stile into the cemetery, my mother's resting place. As I stood at the foot of her grave, I spoke to her as I did every time I visited her grave.

"Hello, Mum, can you speak to Dad for me? Ask him if I can come and live with him?"

With the hope that those words gave me, I turned and climbed back over the stile and headed past the railway cottages and up the hill to the village of whitewashed cottages. The weather was warmer than it had been in the park. As I approached number 14, I could hear the laughter and chatter of my two sisters, who were playing with several other children in the grounds of the village hall. I waved, but did not stop to talk. I did not want to be diverted from the purpose of my visit. Life was too serious for me to be involved in their games, though I longed to feel as carefree as that noisy group.

Pausing at the front door, I decided not to knock, as knocking would have been the action of a visitor. My sisters wouldn't knock. They would be expected to go into their home by the back door. So, I went round the back. I expected my father to be in the garden or sitting in the kitchen. He was not in the garden, but I could see him through the kitchen window sipping a mug of tea and talking to Lizzie. I opened the back door and called, "It's me," as I stepped into the porch. Smiling, Lizzie opened the porch door and I followed her into the kitchen. My father was a heavy Woodbine smoker and, as the door opened, the smoke billowed around me. The smoke rushed up my nostrils and I felt nauseated with the smell. With no welcoming words, he bluntly said, "I hear you're a bit of a sports star." I didn't answer him. I looked straight at him and blurted out, "Can I come and live with you?"

My father did not look surprised and looked at Lizzie. No thoughts were in my head, but I could feel my heart was thumping as my fate was about to be decided.

"Come after school tomorrow. Your mother will have a bed ready for you."

Lizzie said nothing. I breathed out, raised my head, smiled and said, "Thanks." I ran to tell my sisters, who squealed and hugged me, as they were so pleased with my news. An hour later I left to walk back to Annan .... without having eaten a Sunday tea.

******

Moving to the village was easy, as I had few possessions. I packed my football gear, spare underwear and jumper into a suitcase. That was it, I was ready to move. I said to Bella, "Thanks for looking after Grandad and me."

Next day after school, I sneaked into my former home. Aunt Bella did not see me leave as I picked up the suitcase, quietly closing the door behind me. That part of my life was now a closed door. I did not say goodbye to anyone. I'd told them my good news the night before and saw the relief on their faces. Whistling and swinging my suitcase, I walked once more to Cummertrees.

Only Lizzie was at home. My father was still at work and my sisters were out somewhere playing. No welcome ceremony for me; Lizzie just said, "Your bed is ready."

That was enough for me, I opened the door of the bedroom that my sisters slept in. My sisters were now going to share the double bed while I slept in the single. I put the suitcase under the bed and went out of the back door. Outside, I surveyed the surroundings and, tucking my hands in my pockets, went back down the hill to the railway cottages. Jessie was pleased to see me; her hug conveyed her joy. Jessie told me that she'd been coming out of the post office on Saturday afternoon and saw Uncle Alex get off the bus and walk to our house. I did not think much about it at the time; it did not occur to me that he might have gone to visit my father to discuss me.

I did wonder why my father agreed so easily that I could come and live with them. A week later, when I visited Aunt Cathy, she told me the reason: "Alex went to see your father and Lizzie to discuss where you were going to live. During the discussion Lizzie supported you coming to live with them, saying that your father should remember that you had three sisters, and that coming back to live in the village would be good for everyone."

Uncle Alex had told my father that there was no way I was going into a children's home and if living with my sisters did not work out, I could go and live with him and Aunt Cathy at Newbie. My father had reluctantly agreed.

Uncle Alex had not had time to come and tell me the news before I'd walked to Cummertrees the following day. I said to Aunt Cathy, "You mean there was no reason for me to ask my father anything?"

She smiled at me and put an arm around my shoulder. "No," she said. "Now go and put the kettle on."

******

As the weeks passed, my relationship with my father and my new mother made good progress. As we got to know each other I was very careful about what I said and was polite when I spoke to them.

I missed the milk round that I'd done when I lived in the town, but I had plenty of work to do. My father involved me in the jobs he was doing and gave me specific chores. When Dad - who I was starting to think felt more like a dad - came home from work, I would hop on his bicycle and go back to the farm he'd just come from. I'd wait to collect the stainless-steel milk-can, full of newly-pasteurised cold milk, then cycle back home with it. By taking over one of his daily tasks, Dad didn't have to hang around after work to get the family's milk. He could get home earlier.

My sisters and I regained the closeness and love we used to have. This was good for all of us, because I could tell that they did not like their new mother very much. Lizzie, who I avoided calling Mum, had very strict rules, which she enforced with punishment when broken. Treats were few and far between.

The big freeze had left most of the cottages in need of a fresh coat of paint. I was the only boy in the village old enough to do odd jobs. When I whitewashed our house, other people wanted me to do theirs. I could earn between five and ten shillings a week working after school and at weekends.

I knew that I would have to hand over my earnings to Lizzie, so I lied about the money I received; I only declared half the amount, which was duly taken. The rest I hid away beside a gatepost I could access when walking to Powfoot. In my first year back in the village I was never short of work or money. When I was not whitewashing houses, I cut lawns and hedges or dug gardens. At Christmastime, I collected holly and sold it around the villages for decorations. My former employer, Mrs Hendry, asked me to deliver telegrams again. I had the use of her bicycle, which sped up my ability to work. I worked from dawn until dusk and spent my money on new football gear, going to the pictures and buying comics.

As I was so busy, I seldom saw my father or Lizzie. I was happy to be accepted into their house, but other than that, I was an independent person. The people I did depend on were my sisters. They helped me and I helped them. They were proud of my football expertise and assisted in my training. I had obtained an old stopwatch from Bert Lorraine, my PE teacher. My three sisters would time my training runs along Mill Road and onto the Solway sands, and back along the main road past my old primary school, a distance of around six miles. I never changed my route, but often had to change the starting point because of tide times. I was knocking minutes off my overall run time each week.

On the whole, everything seemed to be going well. I was still not sure of my relationship with my father, and there certainly was no bond or closeness between us; however, generally, we existed together comfortably. Our first clash came when I did something really naughty.

It was a beautiful Friday evening and I was out fishing. I'd caught nothing. I decided to do some goalkeeper training by throwing my rubber ball against the wall of the village hall and catching it. I hid my rod in the grass and set off. Five minutes later, I jumped over the wall into the hall grounds and froze. There was activity inside the hall. It suddenly dawned on me that it was the last Friday of the month, when the Women's Rural Institute met in the hall. You did not play bouncy ball for fear of your life when they got together; the women of the W.R.I. were a feisty bunch of ladies, who had many rules and very loud voices.

The only window offering a clear view to what was going on inside was on the far side of the hall. I felt brave enough to go and have a peek. Sure enough they were there, around thirty of them, including Lizzie, all smiling and talking their heads off. As I made my way around the hall, I noticed a window in the ante room was open - the room used to serve tea and sandwiches! What a sight for a hungry lad.

It was easy to get to the window by climbing on to the boiler room roof. From this height I could see right through the window into the room below. The sight inside was just too much of a temptation. There must have been enough food there for more than thirty people. Looking down, the tables were set with plates of freshly-made sandwiches and scones. Folding chairs were set around the walls. It would be easy to get in, just a small step down to the chairs and onto the floor. Once inside, I grabbed some food. I took just enough so that no one would notice anything was missing. I put sandwiches and scones into a brown paper bag that crackled and rustled as I hastily filled it. I stopped and listened; nobody had heard me over the loud voices beyond the door. I thought I'd better get out of there fast. I knew that if I hung around and got caught it would mean a clip round the ear. Worse still, it would mean a good thrashing from my father for stealing. I felt I had enough in the bag to give me a hearty snack and turned to make my escape.

That was when the idea came to me. Turning back and grinning, I emptied the fillings from the sandwiches into some more brown paper bags. I then put the two bits of bread together as if nothing was amiss. Once outside, I realised I had to get rid of the evidence. The bottom of the bag containing the tomato, egg and spam was getting wet. If I stayed much longer the area would soon be strewn with sandwich filling, so I decided to head back to the lake.

I felt great feeding the fish with the sandwich fillings and eating my share of the sandwiches and scones. I was thinking about the women and what would happen when they bit into their sandwiches. What would they say? Whose voice would be the loudest? I smiled to myself. I was visualising the horror on their faces and laughing silently, when it dawned on me that I was now in big trouble. I was the only boy in the village who could be blamed. Who would they think was the culprit? I was the one and only suspect! The thought of Sam the policeman coming to the door and taking me away to jail brought tears to my eyes. Worse still was the thought of the two-inch-wide heavy leather belt that was nearly always around my father's waist.

I did not know where my father was, but after leaving the lake, having fed the evidence to the fish, I sneaked back into my house. I lay in bed pretending to be asleep when Lizzie got home from the W.R.I. meeting. I did not sleep much that night. I could hear Lizzie talking about the missing sandwich filling and my name was mentioned. I thought that I'd be dragged out of bed and questioned, but nothing happened. Sounds of Lizzie and Dad preparing to sleep were all I heard. Sleep evaded me as I listened to my sister's snores and imagined the scenes of my punishment.

Saturday was a half-day at work for my father, but I managed to get out of the house before he left. I had evaded capture and punishment for a while longer. As I tried to sneak in the back door after having checked my snares, there stood Lizzie. There was no chance of getting past her. Silence reigned for a minute then, the only words that squeezed through her tight lips were, "Stay in your room, your father wants to see you when he gets home." There was no escape.

The hours passed slowly. My fear filled the room. I could feel myself trembling and it got worse as each hour ticked by. It seemed a lifetime before the bedroom door finally opened. My father did not ask if I was the sandwich thief. The belt was in his hand and he indicated that I should lay face down on the bed. Tears streamed down my cheeks in anticipation of the pain that I would feel, when I sensed the belt go up in the air. A powerful hand came down and pressed me to the bed and I started to scream. I was no match for my father. The room seemed full of heavy breathing as I heard the belt cutting through the air. The sound of the belt crashing down on to the mattress below my body was lost in my screams.

By the time the belt had crashed into the mattress half-a-dozen times, I realised that I was not in pain, it was fear that had made me scream and sob. My father turned me over on the bed and shouted loud enough for Lizzie to hear, "Let that be a lesson to you." Without another word, he turned and left the room. I knew not to leave the room and that there would be nothing to eat until the next day.

No more was said about my 'thrashing'. I realised that I had been very lucky and decided not to do anything so stupid again. Lizzie did not speak to me for weeks, but that I did not mind. From that time onwards, I spent a lot more time with my father at the farm. I respected the fact that I had done wrong and that he'd seen the funny side and decided not to thrash me. I now wonder: if he had thrashed me, would I have had the same respect for him?

CHAPTER 8

Fun, Tragedy and Coal Dust

My days were full and well spent. Football training was always my priority, but work and earning money was not far behind. With money in your pocket you could do what you wanted and buy what you wanted.

The school football season only stopped when the pitch was frozen, covered in snow or waterlogged. Every Saturday morning, I played for Annan Academy against other secondary schools in Dumfries and Galloway. Because of my obsession with training, the natural progression for me was to play for a county standard team. I played for Dumfries and Galloway against Ayrshire, Lanarkshire and the Borders. It was no surprise when, just before the Christmas holiday, Bert Lorraine told me I'd been chosen to have a trial for the Scottish U14 team, which was due to play Northern Ireland. The trials would start in March. I was over the moon, totally exhilarated at the thought of what these trials could do for my future. Would I become a famous footballer? My Uncle Jimmy was a scout for Carlisle United and had been to see me play against Lanarkshire during one of the county matches. My dream was to play for a professional football team.

I had time on my side and lots of adventures and escapades to encounter. Fun and fortune, or misfortune, were not always encountered on the football pitch.

The area where I was born is close to many historical sites, one of which is Caerlaverock Castle. It is a moated triangular castle that was first built in the 13th century, close to where the River Nith flows into the Solway Firth, and only a few miles from Cummertrees. In those days it was not a tourist attraction with an admission fee, it was just a great place to play. Gangs of us would make our way to the castle and pretend that we were defending it against English invaders.

When the birds were nesting, we collected all kinds of eggs. Close to the castle was where I found my prized yellowhammer and goldfinch eggs. Further on, close to the shoreline, there was an abundance of sea birds. One day, I borrowed Mrs Hendry's bike and, with Ian and Hughie, pedalled along the coast to the point where we could walk along the wetlands to spot the gulls nesting, near to where people went to shoot wild geese. Once there, we removed our plimsolls and socks. We collected species of eggs that we did not already have in our collection. We blew out the yokes by pricking a hole in each end and stacked them neatly into cardboard boxes filled with cotton wool.

Food was always on our minds and we talked about the types of eggs we'd taken home to eat. I had eaten ducks' eggs and waterhens' eggs, but never seagulls' eggs. My mates hadn't tested this delicacy either, so we decided to take some home to try them. After collecting a dozen or so, we carefully stacked them, unblown, into our socks, which we then hung around our necks.

We'd had a great day, so Hughie suggested heading to the lakes to catch a trout, then we'd have fish to cook with the eggs. As we approached the village, Hughie looked back and shouted, "Last to reach the lake is a sissy," before increasing his speed. By the time we reached the top of the hill leading down to the lakes, Hughie was just in front of Ian and I was close to the back wheel of Ian's bike. Halfway down the hill, Hughie realised that we were all going too fast. He squeezed his brakes on too hard. Next thing, Ian had crashed into Hughie's bike and I'd crashed into Ian's. The three of us ended up in the grass, bruised, but with no broken bones. Only our pride was hurt, because we were all covered in broken seagulls' eggs. When I arrived home, Lizzie and Dad looked at me with disgust because of the state I was in, and because I'd damaged Mrs Hendry's bike, which my father would now need to fix.

I was not punished for the egg mishap, because my father

knew that Grandad was very sick and in a serious condition. He told me the sad news as he mended the bike. I was devastated. I didn't have time to see my grandfather again; he passed away the following day. It was just two weeks after my fourteenth birthday, which had been one of the last times we'd spent together, when I'd visited him at Newbie.

If felt like my whole world had fallen apart. I was numb with shock and felt painfully alone. It hurt, knowing that we'd never again chat about boxing or his ferrets. We'd had such a close, friendly life when we'd lived together. He'd taught me so much.

My grandfather's funeral was a simple affair, with only close family and friends in attendance. My father felt that I shouldn't go, but I insisted. Uncle Alex had to help me into the cemetery. After the service I collapsed and had to be carried out to the car outside. So many people had left me or ignored my presence. For weeks I did not talk to anyone.

******

To overcome my grief, I felt I needed to be active all the time. Just before school broke up for Christmas, Jim Steel, who lived next door, asked Dad if I could help out at the coal depot during the holidays. Jim owned the coal business. Without hesitating, my dad agreed. He thought physical activity would take my mind off my grandfather's death and get me back on track with my training. When Dad told me, I was relieved to know that the holidays would not drag. As a bonus, I thought that filling and lifting bags of coal would help to build my muscles and maintain my fitness. Missing my beloved grandfather meant that I'd neglected my football.

Because of the way Christmas and New Year's Day fell that year, school finished on 23rd December and would not re-open until 9th January. This would give me almost three weeks' work. I would earn a lot of money. I rubbed my hands in anticipation of what I could buy or do with such a vast sum. I was fourteen years old, with lots of dreams and wishes.

Before 7:00a.m. on Saturday morning, after school had closed for Christmas, I was already dressed and ready for work. I was eager to start this new venture, feeling happy for the first time in ages. Lizzie had prepared me a sandwich and included a shortbread biscuit. "For your ten o'clock break," was all she said. No 'good luck' or 'look after yourself'. I grabbed my tuck box, ready and willing to start work.

Jim had two men working for him called Davy Sheridan and Bobby Gibb. He had taken on Bobby when the business started to grow. Previously, Bobby had worked in the forests in the north of Scotland before he moved down south. He was strong and able to work with coal. My new workplace, the coal yard, was part of Annan's rail goods yard, where coal wagons were shunted directly into the sidings. Davy, who was seventy years old, bagged the coal while Jim and Bobby did the deliveries. My job was to help Davy with the bagging. I'd been employed because Davy was old and was finding it difficult to climb up into the wagons to shovel the coal forwards when they were nearly empty.

That Saturday morning was the coldest day of the year. As we entered the coal yard, puddles were frozen solid. Bags of coal were stacked, ready for delivery. The sacks were as hard as ice; they looked like they had white ears sticking out of the top. Jim gave me an old pair of woollen gloves that had a Wolsey label on the inside. There was a Wolsey factory in Annan; my Aunt Cathy had worked on the machines that knitted the gloves.

Davy was a good teacher. He showed me how to hook the coal sacks on to scales, which they called an 'iron man'. The apparatus was 5ft high and about 2ft wide, with two hooks to hold the sacks while they were being filled. Getting the correct distribution of coal lumps was difficult at first. If there was too much dross, or the bag contained lumps that were too big or too small, the customers would complain. Getting the balance right was important. Each load on the lorry was four tons, which meant that forty bags had to be filled, weighed and stacked ready for the lorry as it returned twice a day.

By the time Jim and Bobby had driven the empty lorry back into the yard, I was warm from all the physical effort. I had taken my jacket off and put it into a shed that served as an office and tea-room. As soon as we had forty bags ready for collection, Davy gave me a leather back protector and demonstrated how to lift a sack onto my back, how to carry it into a house and how to empty it into a bunker or cupboard. He told me that the secret was to get the bag well up on the shoulders, and then to turn the shoulders so that the bag pressed against a wall and the coal just fell out onto the floor. The bag had to be placed against the wall at the correct height so as not to create too much dust. Davy also showed me how to correctly lift a bag straight onto the flatbed lorry. Within a week of starting, I was the one who went out delivering with Bobby while Jim stayed in the yard to do his paperwork and help Davy.

The coal was delivered to customers in Annan and the surrounding villages – normally, two bags per household. As it was winter and near Christmas, the order was usually three bags per house. Some of the deliveries were difficult; often, the bags had to be carried a long way around the backs of terraces, or up flights of stairs within blocks of flats. Our customers tended to be women who often tried to chat us up. Coal had to be paid for before we deposited an order. The policy was 'no money, no coal'. There was only one time Bobby ignored this rule.

Sarah Livingston lived with her three children in a farm cottage, where they could stay whilst Gerry, her husband, worked on the farm. However, he'd left his farm job for another position in Liverpool and promised to come back for the family when he'd got settled. He'd left in October; now, it was nearly Christmas and she'd not heard from him. Even the welfare people had not been able to trace him. Knowing that our next run included her cottage, Bobby had prepared two bags of dross mixed with bits of coal to drop off at Sarah's. She was having a hard time feeding, clothing and keeping her children warm, so he also donated a bag of wood, some old clothes, four apples and a quarter-pound bag of sweets. He stayed long enough to help her light the fire. When Bobby emerged from the cottage, I heard her say, "Thanks, Bobby. Have a nice Christmas." Her Christmas would be a lot warmer, though still not happy, due to his kindness.

Coalmen only had two days holiday in the cold winter months: Christmas Day and New Year's Day. If Christmas Day fell on a Saturday, they'd have an extra day's holiday on Boxing Day. Luck wasn't with me that year as Christmas Day was on a Sunday, which meant it was back to work for me on Monday morning.

After my first day of work, I'd got a shock when I arrived home. Dad wasn't at home, as he'd gone to get the milk. Outside in the garden stood the tin bath filled with water. I could see that I was not going to be able to wash in the sink in the warm kitchen. I did not protest and moan about the cold; I thought it was Lizzie's way of getting back at me for taking the fillings out of the sandwiches and embarrassing her in front of the W.R.I. I put on a brave face and, dressed only in my underpants, sat down in the freezing cold water and scrubbed myself clean.

My father arrived just as I was getting dried. "What on earth are you doing?" he asked. "You'll freeze to death out here."

Shivering, I replied that I did not mind a cold bath. I was covered in coal dust and I didn't want to spread it everywhere in the cottage. Lizzie watched and listened to our conversation but said nothing herself. No words were exchanged between her and my father in my hearing, but the bath never went into the garden again. She still made sure my brown pay-packet went straight to her hand, though. She'd open it and give me a ten-shilling note for pocket money.

Christmas Day 1955 was a white Christmas in a number of places, but for Cummertrees there was only the odd shower of sleet and rain. During my childhood, Christmas Day was not much different to a normal Sunday, except for the gifts. Children were first out of bed, eager to open their presents. Most children got a main gift plus another smaller one, as well as the usual fruit and sweets. The main present was usually a game or jigsaw puzzle. This year I was lucky; I got a new pair of football boots and a pair of football socks, no doubt from the wages I gave to Lizzie. I had grown so much that my boots were giving me blisters. In our home, Christmas dinner would be different; this year, we would be tucking into goose with all the trimmings.

After some porridge and toast, Lizzie told me and my three sisters to put on our coats, hats and gloves, and to go out and play while she prepared the dinner table in the front room. We trooped out into the damp morning carrying our presents to show the other children, who had also been ushered outside to play while their dinners were prepared.

When Janet's mother called her in for dinner, everyone else knew this was a signal that our meal would soon be ready, and we headed home. In the kitchen there was a basin of water to wash our hands in. As we dried our hands, we basked in the warmth and breathed in the smells from cooking, with excitement and anticipation of the feast to come. Lizzie called us to the front room, so I let my sisters go in first and smiled as I heard their gasps of surprise and amazement. As I entered behind them, Dad was sitting by a roaring fire with a Woodbine between his fingers and a half-empty glass of milk stout by his side. There was a look of contentment on his face. The table looked beautiful. It was covered with a white tablecloth and set with shiny cutlery, with a soup bowl on top of a big plate. A Christmas cracker and two party-poppers rested at the side of each plate, ready for the festive meal.

Everyone enjoyed the dinner. Lizzie had prepared soup with the goose innards, barley, carrots and onions. When the last spoonful of soup had slipped down into our warm bellies, Dad carved the goose and Lizzie put vegetables on the plates. She asked, "Who wants stuffing?"

"Not me, thank you," I said, unlike my sisters who shouted, "Yes, please." Our plates were piled high with the gorgeous goose and vegetables. It was so good. I felt as if I could eat no more, but then I spied the pie.

Was it rhubarb, my all-time favourite? Yes, it was, so I tucked into an enormous slice covered in steaming custard. Everyone else was welcome to eat as much Christmas cake as they wanted, as I did not like currants or raisins. By this time, Dad had drunk two milk stouts, which he had mixed with a bottle of Export beer, a drink which he called a 'black and tan'. He was in a happy mood, which lasted until 8:00p.m. Then, he decided that he'd had enough of I-Spy and snakes and ladders, and left to go to bed. This was a signal that the festivities were over, that we needed to settle down and be quiet; the girls helped to clear up before we all went to bed, giggling and telling stories.

Next day it was back to normal. Dad and I were up and ready for work before the three girls were out of bed. A mixture of sleet and rain greeted us as we left through the back door. I could see that the kitchen light was on in Jim's house, so I backtracked and waited in the kitchen, keeping dry, until I heard his lorry start up. My father just said, "See you tonight," before he pedalled off to work.

CHAPTER 9

The Football Star

Was this going to be my lucky break? The start of my football career? Drew Carruthers, the famous Scottish goalkeeper – could I achieve my dream? The first of the U14 Scottish football trials was to take place on Saturday 3rd March 1956. Four teams from the south of Scotland and four teams from the north of Scotland would compete for places in the final team that would travel to Belfast to play Northern Ireland's U14s. The two games in the south would be played at Gasworks Park Larkhall, a small town in South Lanarkshire, fourteen miles south-east of Glasgow. The second game would be at Somerset Park, the home ground of Ayr United, two weeks later.

I was picked up at the bus stop in Annan at 8:30a.m. by Bert Lorraine, who drove the fifteen miles to Dumfries to meet up with the other players and officials. All of us then boarded the bus to head to Larkhall, which was a smooth, trouble-free journey. In fact, it was quite enjoyable, as one of the officials had brought along a portable radio and everyone sung along to such as Secret Love, This Ole House, Mr Sandman, and a host of other songs. We arrived in plenty of time for the game, which kicked off at 1:30p.m.

After the bus parked up, the players went straight to the dressing room, through the rear door to the pitch where we would play. Groans of dismay echoed through the group as we saw that the pitch was grassless; it was made from ash. I visualised what my body might look like after diving across the goal to save shots. We kitted up and I pulled on my orange goalkeeper's jersey and followed my teammates on to the pitch. Team talk was brief, covering only one topic – no two-footed tackles. Five minutes before the game kicked off, the teams lined up. We all looked very smart when we met the two dignitaries, the referee and two linesmen. I looked around and saw the ground was half-full of local schoolchildren, their parents, and other adults making up the spectators.

An important aspect of a goalkeeper's function is to memorise the names of all his team's defenders. Doing this is important, because the goalkeeper cannot just call for a player to leave the ball for him, he has to use the player's name, otherwise it is a foul. The match ball was plain leather and tied with a leather lace. It looked small and perfectly round, and when I picked it up, it was hard and not too heavy. This was the kind of ball that, when kicked, would come at me with speed. At the end of this match, I knew that it would be either me or the other goalkeeper in the yellow jersey who would be lucky enough to be chosen for a second trial.

The whistle blew and the centre-forward passed the ball to the inside right, who turned it back to Billy, the centre-half and the team captain. Billy turned and drove the ball back to me. Having got a feel for the ball, I bounced it to the eighteen-yard line and kicked it as far as I could beyond the halfway line. From that point on my team were kept under constant pressure. Just before half-time we got our first corner. Billy, our 5 feet 10 inches centre-half, moved up the field. As the ball came across from the corner, he leapt into the air and headed the ball straight past their keeper and into the net. Their goalkeeper had failed in his job and I knew that I was ahead in the stakes for a second trial.

The half-time team talk centred around defending and man-to-man marking. As the second half kicked off, the opposing team came at us with fire in their bellies. No one was worrying about scrapes or bruises; winning was the only thing on our minds. The score remained at one nil until the final whistle blew.

Happy with the result, our blood-smeared team headed to the toilets where a communal shower was installed. As we stripped and plunged under the cold shower, the floor turned red with the blood from cuts we'd received from the ash pitch. We suffered bravely as Bert and another official dabbed our wounds with iodine, or covered them with Germoline antiseptic cream and a bandage.

A few days later Bert informed me that I had been picked for the second trial.

******

Somerset Park is the home of Ayr United; the team was in third place in the Scottish second division. Their stadium had a big stand where around half of the 2000-plus spectators were seated. The other half were scattered around the open-air stands. The second trial kicked off at 12:30 p.m., so that it would be finished before the main game kicked off at 3:00p.m. Spectators were welcome to come early and be entertained by the schoolboys' game before the main match started.

It was a cautious start; no one wanted to make an early mistake and blow their chance of selection. The Ayrshire team settled quickly and we were under pressure. The first goal I let in came from a corner halfway through the first half. The second came just before half-time when the outside right crossed a low ball into the six-yard box and the centre forward slotted the ball home. I thought that I should have stopped the first goal, but I stood no chance on the second. The second half was fairly even and we pulled a goal back. The game was hard fought, the Ayrshire team scoring a third goal five minutes from time when Billy brought down the centre-forward, which resulted in a penalty. I was gutted, and my dream of playing for my country looked to be quickly disappearing.

In PE Bert kept repeating, "No news is good news." But, to me, it meant no news was bad news. Monday morning was agony and I couldn't concentrate on anything. The only thing in my head was the thought that I was a failure. I hardly ever paid attention during English; that day, I did not hear a word Mr Eaglesham, my teacher, said. Suddenly, there was a knock at the door. Mr Eaglesham was a senior teacher, so his class was never interrupted unless it was important. He opened the door just enough to step out. Twenty seconds later, he re-entered the classroom accompanied by Bert, who was smiling in my direction. My spirit soared as he announced that I was going to Boghead, the venue for the final trial.

The following Saturday, 7th April, could not come fast enough. My father had congratulated me and I felt so proud. He was a decent footballer himself and showed his appreciation of my achievements.

Boghead, the home of Dumbarton F.C., was considered to be the oldest football stadium in Scotland. The grounds were well laid out with a stand that had seating, plus standing room. I felt nervous as I came out onto the pitch, dressed this time in a bright-green jersey.

Before we came out, however, the coach, who trained Ayr United's junior team, gave a briefing. He asked me for the names of my five defenders. I knew all of them. Billy and Ian had made it to the final trial and Billy had been named our captain. When we were lined up to meet the officials and dignitaries from the Scottish Schoolboys' Football Association, I began to feel uncomfortable as I eyed up the opposing team. Several of their team were taller than us and those that weren't looked quite tough. Only one of them was what you might call small. I knew from experience that he would be one of the most dangerous players.

The game kicked off and the inside-left passed the ball back to Billy, who passed it straight back to me. The ball felt good as I belted it back up the pitch and my nerves settled down. The north of Scotland had the more skilful players, as most of them had received professional coaching at clubs around Edinburgh or Glasgow. It was a hard battle and the north were 2-0 up at half-time. I did not have time to think that I might make a mistake. The little inside-left and the tall centre-forward were only prevented from scoring five or six times by the hard tackling of Billy and the other defenders. I was thankful Billy was my centre-half and captain. In the second half we started to get on top. Although our players were, on average, smaller, we were fitter and tougher than the city boys from the north. The game ended 3-3.

Almost two agonising weeks passed before Bert came through the open door in the metalwork classroom. All the class looked at Bert in anticipation. After a short chat with Mr McConville, Bert asked me to come to the rector's office. I wondered what I had done wrong. As Bert knocked on the rector's door and waited to hear 'come in' I was confused but hopeful that I was going to get good news and not a telling off. As we entered the room, the rector was already standing up. He shook hands with Bert and smiled before exclaiming, "I am so proud! A pupil from Annan Academy has been selected to represent Scotland at football." My legs wobbled, and I had difficulty holding back tears. Bert told me that I had been chosen as one of the two goalkeepers in the Scotland squad, which would play against Northern Ireland in Belfast on 21st April. I could not believe what I was hearing.

When I returned to class, my mates were overjoyed and full of congratulations. At home my father seemed genuinely pleased. He said that he could not recollect anyone else from Annan Academy realising such outstanding success in football.

******

By 1:20p.m. on Thursday, two days before the match, Bert and I were on the A74 heading for Glasgow. The road was a single carriageway except for two stretches, one at Lesmahagow and the other at Hamilton. Bert had filled the car with petrol before he left, but he stopped at Lesmahagow to fill up again and have a toilet break. Ten minutes later, we set off on the final leg to Glasgow. As we left the A74 and joined the A8 to travel through Glasgow to Lancefield Quay, which was part of Broomielaw, the name given to Glasgow Harbour, we passed a sign for Ibrox Stadium. Bert commented, "Perhaps you'll play there one day."

I gazed with longing at this temple to football, silently wishing for success. Fifteen minutes later, we crossed the Jamaica Bridge and turned left into Broomielaw. As we entered the parking area, we saw a group of boys sporting blue sports bags with the Scotland emblem on them. After parking the car and retrieving our bags from the boot, we followed the boys carrying Scotland bags to the waiting room and joined the other players and officials who had already arrived. After meeting the officials, we sat down for our evening meal before boarding the ship berthed at Lancefield Quay.

Mr Wintergoose, the director of Scotland Schools' Football, told us that we would not be eating on board as it was a late sailing time and we had to be in bed early to get a good night's sleep. After dinner, one of the officials opened a box and pulled out navy-blue tracksuits. Our correct size would be brought to us in our cabins, assuming our representatives – in my case, Bert – had provided them with the correct measurements. From the next morning onwards, we would only wear this tracksuit; it was our football uniform, which marked us out as representatives of our country.

CHAPTER 10
The Big Game

Once on board, a hatless crew member dressed in a smart blue-and-red uniform introduced himself as Bob Shaw. His role was to familiarise us with the ship's layout and emergency procedures and show us our quarters. Our bags would be delivered to our cabins during our tour. We entered a room, where we sat at a table that could hold up to twenty people. Bob remained standing, like a teacher in front of a class. The name of Burns and Laird was on all the pictures of ships and holiday posters lining the walls. A blue rectangular flag bearing a gold lion, rampant, crowned and holding a globe, was in one of the picture frames.

Bob told us the ship was built by Harland and Wolff at Belfast for the Burns and Laird Lines. It launched on 11 March 1936 as a passenger and cargo ferry in the Irish Sea, operating between Belfast and Glasgow. It was named the Royal Scotsman. A sister ship called the Royal Ulsterman was built at the same time; she also sailed on the Glasgow to Belfast route. Unlike their predecessors, the ships had only one funnel, which gave them a smart, modern appearance. Bob went on to explain that the ship was 3000 GRT, Gross Register Tonnage, which is a ship's total internal volume expressed in register tons. Gross Register Tonnage uses the total permanently enclosed capacity of the vessel as its basis for volume. This was too high-powered and factual for us boys and one put his hand up. Bob stopped talking and asked, "Yes, what's your question?"

"What are the stripes on your arm? What do they mean?"

A bit taken aback, Bob cleared his throat and said, "It's like this. Uniforms display rank and are a source of pride for their wearers. Many seamen in the merchant navy were never required to wear a uniform. When large shipping companies started to carry passengers it became necessary to introduce a uniform and a system of stripes and badges. These helped to identify crew from passengers, officers from seamen or ratings, as well as encouraging discipline."

Bob finally ended our questions and continued with his brief by explaining the safety drill and how to put on our life vests should the ship start to sink. Billy, who had now become my friend, look startled and said, "The ship isn't going to sink, is it?"

Seeing the worry in Billy's eyes, Bob made a joke of it. He replied, "It hasn't sunk in the last twenty years, so I don't think it is going to sink today."

We all laughed and Billy looked relieved. He might have been an excellent footballer, but perhaps he couldn't swim! Bob told us that it would take twelve hours to sail to Belfast and that we had to be in bed with lights out at 22:00. Breakfast was at 07:00. Puzzled, we all stared at Bob. Finally, someone asked, "What's 22:00?"

Bob explained that it meant ten o' clock at night, and 07:00 was seven o'clock in the morning.

That ended our session and we were shown our cabins. They had two double bunks with a single locker and no porthole. Four boys – Danny, Jamie, Billy and me – were sharing. We sat on our bunks, chatting about football, the match, and anything that came into our heads, as we got to know each other. Danny and Jamie were from Glasgow; and Billy, from Ayr. When I said I was from Annan, I had to explain where this was. They understood when I said it was only eight miles from Gretna Green.

Friday morning, and my group was amongst the first to take our place for breakfast. After breakfast, Mr Robertson, who had taken over the organising, told us to collect our bags and make our way to the foot passenger disembarkation exit, where we would board the coach that would take us to the Encore Hotel. The coach was a nice, modern 45-seater, painted blue and white with a banner on the back window that read, 'Scotland Schools' Football', with the Scottish emblem in two of the corners. I felt excited as I took my seat next to the window on the left side of the coach.

As it pulled out of the harbour and onto the main road, I noticed that the area looked old and run-down. It was nothing like Annan with its sandstone buildings and new housing estates. We passed children playing with an old bedstead, and others playing football with an old, leather ball. The boys were all in short trousers, shirts and pullovers, and some looked as if they were not wearing shoes. The girls wore dresses that were hanging from their skinny bodies and looked as if they had never been washed. They stopped playing and waved and shouted as we left them behind.

When we were standing outside the hotel, Mr Robertson gave the instruction that everyone had to be in the hotel restaurant at 12:30p.m. for lunch. We would then be taken by coach to one of the training grounds used by Linfield F.C. players. When he dished out shirts and shorts, I knew that the final team would be selected after this training session. I was also aware that when I pulled on my boots they felt tight. My right foot felt as if the skin was rubbing against the leather, causing me pain.

The training session went well, but not as well as I'd hoped. John Spencer, the other goalkeeper, pulled off some brilliant saves compared to me. At my end of the pitch, I'd had little action and was relieved because my heel hurt so much. Once the training session had finished and the final team was announced, I felt disappointed, but knew that if I had been picked I would have had to tell Mr Robertson that I was injured. The blister on my heel was preventing me from playing to the best of my ability.

Back at the hotel, limping, I made my way to my room to prepare for dinner at 6:00p.m. As I pulled on my socks, I showed Billy my heel, which was now a bloody mess. Billy said, "Don't worry, I'll sort that – no problem." He went to his bag and pulled out some plasters, a bandage and a tube of ointment. Billy said that this was his football first aid kit that his dad had given to him. He found a large plaster that covered the damaged skin perfectly. When I put my shoe on I felt no pain and thanked Billy.

******

Our big day finally arrived. I felt saddened that I was not the number one goalkeeper, particularly since Billy's ointment and plaster seemed to have done the trick and my damaged heel felt much better.

After breakfast we gathered for a team talk, given by Mr Robertson and Mr Burney, who were both dressed in the same style of tracksuit as me. Mr Robertson got everyone's attention by saying, "Okay, lads, team talk time." Silence followed.

Mr Burney spoke next. He went on to discuss tactics, and how we could achieve victory. Finally, he turned to the three reserves, one forward, one defender and me, the reserve goalkeeper. He said that substitutes were not permitted unless there was a bad injury. "These Irish lads are tough and will tackle hard, so if anyone gets hurt, you three have got to be ready." He asked us if there were any questions, but nobody spoke. We just wanted to be on the pitch.

We boarded the bus at 11:15a.m. for a 12:30p.m. kick-off. We were in the Linfield F.C. visitors' dressing room twenty minutes later. We changed into a brand-new Scotland strip: blue shirts with white collars, and the Scotland emblem on the left breast; white shorts and blue-and-white socks. The goalkeepers, John Spencer and I, wore yellow goalkeeper jerseys.

When the teams met to come out, I could see that the Irish boys were dressed in the traditional green shirts of Ireland, plus green shorts and green-and-white socks. They looked to be much smaller in stature than us, the Scottish lads. The only exception was the goalkeeper who was the biggest in the team, a little taller than my mate Billy. The two schoolboy teams walked onto the pitch and the crowd erupted. Five thousand Irish school children, their teachers, and the Irish team's parents were shouting and cheering encouragement. The rest of the stadium was packed full of people waiting to see the main game – the cup final. I was told later that the attendance at the match was more than twenty thousand people. I was overawed by the sight and sound of so many.

The drill was the same as for the trials, which gave a touch of familiarity to the proceedings and settled our nerves a little as we met the dignitaries and the officials. The most important and skin-tingling difference was that this time we stood quietly for the national anthem before splitting into the two halves to warm up.

Match time was soon upon us. The referee and linesmen stood in the middle with Billy and the Irish captain. A coin was tossed to exchange pennants and choose ends. Scotland won the toss and chose to start with the stand on their left. I sat in the dugout with Mr Robertson, Mr Burney, and the other two reserves. The crowd bellowed out loudly, "IRELAND! IRELAND!"

When the players lined up for the kick-off and the whistle blew, the Scottish team attacked. Scotland had got their instructions at their pre-match talk: attack, attack, attack and take no prisoners. It was going to be a hard game.

After twenty minutes, the Scottish goalkeeper had hardly touched the ball and the Irish goalkeeper had pulled off three brilliant saves. Approaching half-time there were no goals. Scotland was on top, but the Irish were starting to fight back. Half-time came – still no score.

The team talk repeated the pre-match briefing, with the added encouragement of, "You're on top. Get a goal and you will kill them off." The first casualty came early in the second half. Billy had slid in and brought down the inside-left who failed to get up right away. He was helped to the side-line by the Irish trainer and was replaced. Ten minutes later the Irish goalkeeper, who had played brilliantly, was beaten by a low power drive from Scotland's centre-forward. The stadium fell silent. Scotland were 1-0 up.

The Irish started to pile on the pressure and were awarded a free kick just outside the eighteen-yard line. John Spencer, expecting the ball to come in high, had seen it too late and the substitute Irish inside-left drove the ball hard and low inches inside John's right hand post. Changing direction, John reacted immediately, got a hand to the ball, and pushed it round the post. The crowd showed their appreciation for the save, but poor John had smashed his shoulder into the goalpost. Two minutes later, he was on a stretcher being carried off. I stripped, warmed up and stood in goal, ready for the corner that had been given.

This could be my moment of glory, or I could prove an utter failure. The corner came in high enough for me to go and meet it and pick the ball out of the air before anyone could touch it. I'd made my mark on the proceedings and I felt good. There was twenty minutes to go and my team were sticking to our instructions of 'attack, attack and keep attacking'. A one goal lead was not enough to feel secure. We piled on the pressure, but the Irish defence remained steadfast. Their goalkeeper was having an exceptional game. He was playing a blinder.

There were barely three minutes to go, plus time the referee added for the two injuries. I was feeling comfortable, I had made a couple of decent saves and was ready for anything. The Irish team were making a last-ditch effort. Seconds later their centre-forward knocked Billy to the ground before making his way to shoot at goal. I was expecting him to take the shot and was ready for it, but he did not kick the ball. Instead, he slipped the ball past the left-back to their inside-right, a good move on their part as it left my goal exposed. The inside-right hit the ball first time and it was heading for the inside of the post. My reaction was instantaneous and I turned to my left and dived. I felt my left hand touch the ball and push it to the outside of the post and behind for a corner.

Billy grabbed me by the shoulders and yelled, "Well done!" Even the Irish players and supporters appreciated my save. I stood in the goal mouth ready for the corner and once again I caught it out of the air before anyone else could reach it. I bounced the ball to the eighteen-yard line and belted it as far up the field as I could get it. I did not touch the ball again and the game finished 1-0, a victory to Scotland.

Everyone whooped and hollered at our success as we shook hands with the Irish boys and went to take our shower. We stowed our kit in the bus before heading to the reserved area for the Cup Final. The spectators clapped both teams and patted us on the back as we passed to take our seats.

We automatically chose to mix the seating arrangement. It ended up with an Irish player sitting beside a Scottish one. The two injured players had recovered sufficiently to join their teams. John Spencer's arm was in a sling. The two Irish goalkeepers sat next to John and me and I had difficulty understanding what they were saying. Perhaps they had the same problem with my accent.

After the formalities, the Irish Cup game kicked off. It was a bit of an even affair, resulting in a 2-2 draw. Once the game was over the boys headed for their coaches saying to each other, "See you tonight for dinner." What a day it had been. I was so proud of my team and myself.

******

Still glowing from my success, I washed and dressed in my grey flannel trousers, white shirt and the blazer that Dad had bought me at a jumble sale. With a final smooth down of my hair, I was ready for the feast and trophy presentation.

"Wear this with pride tonight at dinner, lads!" announced Mr Robertson as he handed out blue-and-white Scottish team ties. At 6:20p.m. we boarded the coach and headed for the Copper Kettle restaurant, a journey of barely ten minutes.

After dinner the waitresses took no time in clearing away the plates as most of them were wiped clean! Once the tables were clear, the waitresses refilled our glasses with beer or lemonade and topped up the teapots. Someone tapped a glass to call for silence and the man sitting next to Mr Robertson stood up and addressed the top central table. He thanked the Scottish Schools' Football Association's chairman for providing an entertaining and hard-fought game. He reflected on the match, praising both sides, and added that my save was crucial to Scotland, as it gave us the victory. He then invited the two chairmen to present the trophy and caps to the players. Everyone cheered as the trophy was handed to the Scottish captain, who proudly raised it high in the air. What an amazing, triumphant day it was.

Sunday was a day of rest and the shops were closed. Mr Robertson told us that we could have a day off, to laze around the town and hotel, or we could go on the coach to the beach for ice-cream. We were all lured by the thought of ice-cream and the freedom and fun that a day on the beach could offer.

As the coach rolled out of the city and into the countryside I could see a big difference in the outlook. The city was dull and dirty while the countryside was similar to what I was used to: farms and villages with churches, village shops and pubs. We reached Ballygally Beach in just over an hour. There were stunning views along the Antrim coastline and dramatic scenery all around. I thought it was the most beautiful beach I had ever seen. It was even more beautiful than Powfoot as its sand was soft and golden. It was just like Aunt Cathy had described when she told me about Achill Island.

There were two ice-cream vans, towards which we all headed when we got off the bus. No one was swimming in the sea, but the beach was crowded. Dressed in our Scotland tracksuits, we were the centre of attention. One family said that they had seen us play and they thought it was a better game than the Cup Final.

After an hour-and-a-half we headed back, taking a different route back to the hotel. We stopped to look at Glenarm Castle and Gleno Waterfall, then passed through Larne before our day trip ended. Just before we left the bus, Mr. Robertson told us that the following day we were going on an official tour of Belfast; he suggested we got a good night's sleep as it would be another long day. The rigours of our match, plus the relaxing sea air, resulted in Billy and me falling asleep around 9:30p.m.

******

We were on the bus ready to go by 9:15a.m. Last to board was Mr Robertson and a lady dressed in a green skirt and white top. He introduced her as Colleen O'Donnell. She was our guide for the day.

The first attraction was the docks, where we saw ships being built. Next was the pier where Irish immigrants sailed for America. Colleen explained a bit about the history of shipbuilding in Belfast. I could see huge cranes lifting metal sheets while men riveted and welded them to the hull. It looked noisy, hard and cold work; I felt that working in the docks would not be for me.

Leaving the dock area, we passed by the Customs office and headed back into the city. On the way we stopped for a few minutes at the Albert Clock, which Colleen explained was erected in 1865, in a gothic style to commemorate Queen Victoria's consort, Prince Albert. She added that it was 113ft tall, and that if you climbed to the top you would be able to see right across the city and all the dock area. I had no idea what she meant by gothic style so I kept quiet.

By the time we reached Stormont - which was very impressive and surrounded by wonderful gardens - I was starving. I was relieved when sandwiches were given out.

Colleen explained that the Stormont building had perfect symmetry and symbolism. The building was 365ft wide, which represented one foot for every day of the year; it had six floors and six pillars at the entrance, one for each county of Northern Ireland.

The tour finished just before 3:00p.m., and after a 45-minute return journey, we pulled up at the hotel. Mr Robertson said a few words about the marvellous tour and called for a round of applause. We all clapped in appreciation of our wonderful day and waited for Colleen and the other officials and dignitaries to leave the bus. Mr Robertson came back on board and told us that we had to come down for dinner in our civilian clothes, ready to go to the boat at 5:00p.m. We were going home!

******

At the docks, we thanked the driver and everyone headed into the departure lounge. Mr Robertson told us that we were going back on the Royal Ulsterman, which was the sister ship to the one we'd sailed out on. At 8:10p.m., having felt the ship pull out, my three roommates and I headed to the main deck. Along with a group of about fifty others, we spent the next hour watching Belfast fade into the distance. I felt sad and wondered if I would ever see Belfast again. On the way back to our cabins, I bought a wall plate souvenir for Dad and Lizzie and sweets for my sisters. I was asleep by 10:00p.m.

With faces washed and sports bags at the ready, my group were sitting down at breakfast when we heard the public address speaker barking out that passengers had to prepare to disembark now. We gobbled down the remains of our toast, had a last slurp of tea and grabbed our bags. After disembarking, we headed straight for the lounge, where the chairman gave a short farewell speech. Then it was handshakes and goodbyes all round before Bert and I set off for his Ford Prefect car. It was where we left it and it started at the first attempt.

We were back at Annan Academy just before lunch. I thanked Bert for taking me to Ireland. He told me that I could go straight home if I wished, but I said I'd go to my metalwork class as there would be no one at home. That was not true. I just wanted to see my friends and tell them all about Ireland. Bert took the sports bag and told me to pick it up from the staff-room after the final bell went.

Everyone was pleased to see me back, and when I told them that Scotland had won, there was cheering and whistles of congratulation.

Dad had arrived from work at 5:15p.m. and had finished his tea before I returned. He told me that he'd heard Scotland had won then said, "You must be pleased and proud."

It was then I remembered the plaque and sweets in my sports bag, so I went and got them out of my bag and gave them out. I suddenly realised that I had bought nothing for myself! When Dad went to the village hall later that night, my sisters and I shared the sweets. They thought that my accent was funny. Why they thought this, I do not know. Surely, a few days away in Ireland couldn't have changed me that much!

CHAPTER 11

The Man in the Hat

My birthday landed on September 8th, six days after the summer school leaving deadline; because of this, I had to stay at school for another term. Bert asked me to stay on for a further full year, so that I could take part in the U16 Scotland football trials. However, as much I loved football, I knew that this option would never be agreed. My father's view was that it was time to pay my way in life: time to start earning money. I never discussed Bert's option with anyone because I already had a job. Jim Steel had offered me one as a coalman when I left school. My future was mapped out for me … or so I believed.

When school restarted after the holidays, I took time off whenever Jim needed me in the coal depot or to go out delivering with Bobby. Nobody seemed to check up on me from school. I could earn five pounds a week and ten shillings extra for working Saturday mornings. The latter amount was a bonus; Jim said, "Don't tell Lizzie about it."

He said that, because he knew that most of my money was taken from me to pay for my keep, but the bonus was mine to splurge in any way I desired.

Up to that point, I had only made one mistake in my job, and that was when I carried a second bag of coal up the stairs to a flat in Lady Street. Bobby had warned me not to create any dust as the lady was very house-proud, but on the way out from the coal cupboard I forgot to turn the bag the right way up and dropped coal dross and dust on her polished floor. Mrs Collins was not a happy woman. She made me sweep and polish the floor before I left. I was always doubly careful after that, as my mistake made us late in our delivery run. I didn't want to lose my job. When Bobby told Jim what had happened I was not fired, and Jim and Bobby had a good laugh.

Fridays were always good days, as work started an hour earlier and finished as soon as the second lorry load had been delivered. The pubs were open all day on Friday as it was market day, when farmers from all over the region came to Murray Street, to buy and sell cattle and sheep. Once they'd finished their business, they went straight to one of the three pubs located on the high street. Jim would buy us, his workers, minced lamb or beef pies from Mrs Halbert's pie shop. He'd then take Bobby and Davy to the Buck Inn for a drinking session before they went home. Being underage, I was not allowed in the pub, so, at that point in the day, I'd catch the bus back home. If the weather was warm, I'd take the tin bath into the garden and scrub myself clean. My stepmother hated the coal dust that came into the house from my clothing and boots.

In my opinion, the fourth year at school was boring and I had little interest in learning. All the teachers realised that boys like me, whose birthday landed after September 1st, were just killing time before they left school at Christmas. Mr Sewell, the music teacher, thought that the best way to keep us from being unruly was to allow us to play football. Therefore, when I did go to school, I always took my football kit with me.

As the class lined up outside the music classroom, expecting Mr Sewell to arrive from the staff-room, I was surprised to see him open the music room door from the inside and step out. With a smile on his face, he announced that there would be no football today.

Billy Kennedy, one of my closest mates, commented gruffly, "Aw! We're not going to do music are we, sir?"

"No," was the reply, "something more interesting." With no more explanation, he walked back into the room. We followed behind and sat at our usual desks.

We started chattering and Mr Sewell allowed it to go on, because we were looking at and discussing the posters on the walls. I had been a member of the Air Cadet Corps (ATC) for a short time and recognised some of the aeroplanes that were on display. A knock at the door quietened us down and heads turned, as we expected to see the headmaster stride into the room. We were wrong. Instead of him, a large uniformed man stepped through the door and shook Mr Sewell's hand. Billy Kennedy turned to me and whispered, "Who's the man in the hat?" I replied quietly, "He's an RAF officer. I recognise the uniform from the ATC."

Mr Sewell turned to the now-quiet class and introduced the man in the hat as Flight Lieutenant Thompson. The flight lieutenant explained that he had been a pilot during the war, but now he was in charge of recruitment, and that more members of his team were visiting other schools in the area.

After telling us what the RAF had achieved during the war and showing photographs of the Battle of Britain, he opened the flight bag he'd put on the table and took out a handful of forms. He told us that this was a dangerous time and war could once again affect the world, only this time it would be between us and Russia or China.

A map of the world was on the wall and he pointed to the two countries and said, "These are our new enemy and we have to defend our homeland against them. The reason I am here is because I am looking for recruits to join the RAF."

He started to distribute enrolment forms to the class and his final remark was, "If you want to join up you need to get approval from your parents. Get them to sign your form."

I wanted to hear what my mates thought about the RAF. Billy Kennedy and Will Smith said that they were not interested. One of my classmates, 'Huff Huff', commented that he had an apprenticeship to become a joiner, and Hugh Hunter said he was going to join the police. David Francis said there was no chance of him joining up as he was going to work in his father's bakery. I said nothing, as I was now having second thoughts about becoming a coalman.

When my father came in from work his tea was ready, and I knew better than to say anything until he had finished his meal and had washed and changed. It was carpet bowls for him on Tuesday nights and I was anxious to show him the RAF form; I decided to put it on the table where he could see it. Sure enough, he picked it up and asked, "What's this, then?"

I explained that it was a form to join the RAF that I'd been given at school from a man in uniform.

My father briefly read the form and said, "This is to join up as a boy entrant."

"The man told me I could join up at fifteen and do two years' training before joining the real RAF."

My father replied, "If this is what you want to do, it's okay with me. I'll fill in the form and sign it, but it'll have to wait until after my bowls' night."

I had expected a different reaction to my plan and was pleased that no anger or upset was apparent. I said, "Thanks," and headed to the lake to check my fishing rod.

Less than three weeks after I posted the form, a letter arrived with instructions to go to Sauchihall Street in Glasgow on the following Tuesday for an interview to join the RAF Boy Entrants. Inside the envelope was a voucher for a train ticket.

******

When I arrived at Glasgow Central I had no idea which way to go. I made my way out of the train station in the hope that I would see Sauchihall Street and the recruitment centre. A man who looked about the same age as my father asked me if I needed help. When I told him where I was going, he said he'd take me there as he was going in that direction. Twenty minutes later he said, "This is it, and I want a shilling for showing you the way."

Fear gripped me and I began to panic. The man was very insistent and threatened what he would do to me if I did not give him the money. I put my hand in my pocket to pay just as I saw someone come out of the door of the recruitment office. This gave me an opportunity to escape, so I ran as fast as I could into the building before he could react.

Once inside I recovered quickly. I was amazed at the height of the ceiling and the décor on the walls. Sitting on chairs in the entrance hall was a dozen young boys, some with parents or friends who had come to support them. They were all chatting amongst themselves, so I went to join them. Half-an-hour later, an attractive woman wearing a black skirt and white top announced that we were to go for interviews and tests. She told the parents to come back in two hours then said, "Follow me, boys."

Ten minutes later, after we had been led to a room and were seated at single tables, I was filling out a form. I did not understand some of the questions, so naturally I asked for clarification so that I knew what I had to write down. Next came a test paper, which I understood better because I had done similar tests at school. Most of the questions were maths and English, and I answered them as well as I could.

Two hours later, I was sitting on the same chair as before in the waiting room, but this time with two new friends, Jimmy Laurie and Mike Robertson, plus some of the other boys whose names I did not know. The woman in the black skirt and white top directed everyone to go back to the room upstairs and take a seat. A few minutes later, an important-looking man dressed in a dark suit, white shirt and black tie came in and stood in front of the invigilator's desk, facing everyone in the room. I realised that I recognised him - it was the uniformed man in the hat who had visited my school.

Flight Lieutenant Thompson offered his congratulations to me and the other boys; we'd passed the test and were now eligible to join the RAF. We were to travel to RAF Cosford to complete medicals and other formalities, which would take four days.

The train would leave Glasgow Central at 18:30. Another man in uniform, Corporal Anderson, remarked that this was the 24-hour clock, and that only one recruit had got the 24-hour-clock question correct in the test. I knew that was me. He instructed everyone to know the 24-hour clock by the time we reached Wolverhampton.

The journey seemed to take forever and most of the small talk concentrated on backgrounds, the stations the train stopped at, and what we thought about joining the RAF. The 24-hour clock did not enter into any small talk. Corporal Anderson came by to check us whenever the train stopped. When we stopped at Carlisle I knew I was close to home, but my attention had been captured by the packet of sandwiches I'd been given.

After an uncomfortable night, we left the train at Wolverhampton and boarded the waiting bus. At 06:40 we arrived at RAF Cosford's main gate. In no time at all, we were lining up for a meal of porridge, eggs, bacon, sausage and beans, with as much toast as we wanted. I was given 'irons', their term for cutlery, to eat with and a plain-white ceramic drinking mug. The cookhouse was full of boys dressed in civilian clothes. I guessed that they were also new recruits from different regions of the UK. I could see around twenty young boys in uniform who looked the same age or just a bit older than me, who were still eating their breakfast at a nearby table. One of the boys leaned over and said, "Welcome, sprogs, make sure you give a good cough." I soon found out what that meant.

After breakfast we were rounded up and taken for our medical. This was straightforward and comprised of eye, hearing and lung function tests. As I had been advised, I gave a good cough when asked. When it was my turn for the verbal interview, Jimmy Laurie was sitting at the next table. The officer conducting the interview asked a lot of questions about school and sports. I told them all about my football and athletic achievements. The officer noted everything down, looking up at me often, as if he was very interested. I thought I had impressed him.

Finally, the officer asked me what type of training I wanted to do in the RAF. This baffled me a bit, because I had just assumed that I would just 'join'. I had not considered what I would do within the organisation. Puzzled, I looked at the officer and said, "I don't know." He explained my options. I could join the RAF regiment, the catering corps, or become a tradesman. Looking round, I could see that Jimmy had finished and was about to leave. I leant over and asked, "Jimmy, what job are you going to do?"

He replied, "My father is an electrician, so I'm going to be an aeroplane electrician." With no hesitation, I turned and told the officer, "I want to be an electrician."

I had made my future career choice. The officer wrote down 'Electrical Fitter (Air)' on the form.

The final procedure of the day was to 'sign up', which meant writing my signature on the RAF contract. This was done on a separate form and witnessed by the same officer. The contract stated: 'Period of enlistment – nine years from the age of eighteen, followed by three years in the reserves.' I signed my life away on that dotted line. Before I left, I also signed for a packet that contained two pounds and eight shillings. These were my expenses, which would cover my journey back to Scotland.

I arrived home at 09:20a.m. on Friday morning and took the day off school. When Lizzie came in she just said, "Oh, you're back. Tea will be ready in half-an-hour."

There was little reaction from my sisters; I don't think they realised what I had done. I was wondering what my father would say when he came in from work. When he came into the kitchen he asked if I'd had a good journey and if I'd signed up. When I told him that I had his only comment was, "Good, probably the best thing for you." I expected more, but all he added was, "Probably better than being a coalman."

When I got to school on Monday morning I told no one that I'd signed up. I did tell Jim Steel, who said, "You've made the right choice."

******

My joining instructions arrived by post on 1st February 1957, less than two months after I officially left school. They were short and to the point. I was to report to RAF St Athan on

Tuesday 12th February. There was also an information letter containing the details of my enlistment, which included information about the length of service I'd signed up to do, with an option to sign up for twenty-two years after I completed three years of service. Further information stated that my clothes would be returned by post to my home address within seven days of my arrival at St Athan. Also, being under 16, I would not be allowed to smoke without the written permission of a parent or guardian; I would be given a smoking permission form to apply for this after my arrival at the base. So many rules and I was not even there yet!

The last piece of paperwork was a voucher to present at the local railway station up to three days before my travel date, so that my rail tickets could be issued. I did not fully understand how my life would change. I was not really sure what I had done. What I did feel was the excitement of knowing that I was 'joining up' and becoming part of a well-respected organisation.

On 11th February, my father and I caught the 5:50p.m. bus to Annan. There had been no farewell party; in fact, very little had been discussed between us about my enlistment. The only other person who expressed an opinion was Uncle Alex, who was unhappy that I was joining the RAF and not the Kings' Own Scottish Borderers, as this had been his regiment and the regiment that Annan men traditionally joined. If they had visited my school before the RAF came, perhaps that would have been where I ended up!

When we got off the bus, my father and I walked to the junction at the Corner House Hotel. Dad stopped, turned to me and said, "Take this." He handed me a ten-shilling note, which I took and placed in my pocket. My father held out his hand and I shook it. He said, "Good luck," and walked off up the high street. I wasn't surprised that he left me this way rather than say goodbye on the railway platform. I crossed the road and headed for the station, carrying my worldly possessions in my Scotland bag. When the train stopped, I could feel a lump in my throat and tears on my cheeks as I stepped into the cold, empty carriage.

There was a long road ahead of me.

The cottage where my family lived

Inside the Church as it is today

Inside the Church Today

Memorial Plaques inside Mausoleum

SACRED TO THE MEMORY OF
FRANCIS WILLIAM BOUVERIE DOUGLAS
AGED 19, WHO WAS KILLED ON THE 14TH JULY 1865
IN DESCENDING THE MATTERHORN, AFTER HIS
SUCCESSFUL ASCENT. HIS BODY WAS NEVER
RECOVERED.

THERE — STARS WILL EVER SHED THEIR LIGHT.
THE SUN WILL GILD EACH RISING MORN;
HIS WINDING SHEET — THE GLACIER BRIGHT,
HIS MONUMENT — THE MATTERHORN.

"NOT LOST BUT GONE BEFORE."

FOR I KNOW THAT MY REDEEMER LIVETH, AND THAT
HE SHALL STAND AT THE LATTER DAY UPON THE
EARTH. AND THOUGH AFTER MY SKIN WORMS DESTROY
THIS BODY, YET IN MY FLESH SHALL I SEE GOD.
JOB. XIX. 25, 26.

RLES.
QUEENSBERRY

SACRED TO
ARCHIBALD W

The Scotland Under 14 Team 1956

PART 2

CHAPTER 12

The Sprog

I was not sure if I was doing the right thing as I produced the rail warrant. The station-master issued me with a single ticket for my journey from Annan to Cardiff. I felt sick and afraid, but knew in my heart that returning home was not an option. When I got off the train at Carlisle station my stomach felt knotted up and I had no idea where I was going. Eventually I asked a man dressed in a rail uniform which platform I should head towards to catch the train for Crewe.

Fifteen minutes later, I was on the train searching the compartments for Jimmy Laurie and Mike Robertson , who I had befriended at the interview in Glasgow. There was no sign of them. I did recognise two other boys who had been to Glasgow and Cosford with me, but I could not remember their names. They were the only two passengers in the compartment so I asked if I could join them. They told me that their names were David Murray and John Baxter. We shook hands and settled down for the twelve-hour journey to Cardiff.

When the train arrived at Crewe we had time for a cup of tea and a hot sausage roll before our next train left for Cardiff. By the time we boarded the train, our group had grown from three to twelve, all going to St Athan. There was still no sign of Jimmy and Mike.

On boarding the train, we got three compartments between us that were all in the same carriage. During the journey, we moved between compartments and chatted with each other. From these conversations, I realised that I was not the only one who had second thoughts about joining the RAF.

When I left the train at Cardiff station, I saw some people

in RAF uniform who looked like they were waiting for us, so we walked over to meet them. We were directed to the outside of the rail station, where three buses and two trucks were waiting. I did as I was directed and gave my luggage to two people behind one of the trucks and, along with my new friends, boarded one of the buses. An hour later, after some more boys had joined us, we headed to St Athan. I did not have a watch, but I guessed that it was around 11:00a.m. because I felt hungry.

The bus stopped outside the guard room after passing the barrier at the entrance to RAF St Athan. Our escort told us to line up in three rows on the road. The escort was quite nice and guided us on the correct way to do this.

An imposing man, at least six-feet tall, came out of the guard room door. I had seen service policemen on film, but this guy looked frightening. He was dressed in an RAF uniform, but his hat had a white top and he wore a white belt and white gaiters above his highly-polished boots. On his arm was a red-and black armband imprinted with the initials 'SP'. The peak of his cap came straight down; he had to lift his head backwards to be able to see. He had two stripes on his arm, which I knew meant he was a corporal. As the SP approached the group I felt like hiding, but there was no place to hide.

"Listen up, you lot!" he barked, "you need to sign the arrivals book and collect your bedding from the quartermaster, then make your way to G Lines where you can pick up your luggage and settle in."

He turned around smartly and I joined the line at the guard room window to sign in. When my turn arrived, I looked into the guard room and could see a polished floor and what looked like a number of cells beyond an open door towards the back. Our escorts waited until we had all signed in and escorted us to a building near the guard room. There was a sign that said 'quartermaster' on the wall. Once inside, we were issued with five blankets, two sheets, one pillow-case, two towels and a mug and irons. I signed for my bedding and went outside to join the others. Our escorts, who didn't introduce themselves, lined us up outside. One said, "Okay, lads, follow us."

'G Lines' were quite close by, so it took only five minutes to reach them. I knew when we were there because there was a sign with an RAF emblem on it that said 'Initial Training Squadron', and below that, 'G Lines'. Our escort told us to stop and face him. He said that, when your name was called, you had to go inside, find your billet, put your bedding on the bed then come out again and collect your luggage. He added, "You can then go and eat, but be outside on the road again at 13:30, at which time you will be introduced to your drill instructors." He started to read out names and billet numbers from a sheet of paper.

I had been allocated G6, where there were 16 beds, ten of which were now occupied. I selected a bed and placed my bedding and irons on the mattress and went out to collect my bag. David Murray was in the same billet as me, but John Baxter was in the one next door. I sat on my bed thinking, "This room is more crowded than the bedroom I shared with my sisters!"

******

When I entered the cookhouse, I spotted more boys in civilian clothes sitting at the tables. The serving area had a long stainless-steel counter with trays full of food set into the servery, and more food in pots on the top. Men, dressed in blue-and-white checked trousers with white coats and hats, were serving food. A similarly-dressed man, with corporal stripes on his coat, supervised the activities. I could see more boys dressed in uniform lining up along another servery in what looked like a separate cookhouse, but which was in the same building.

I picked up a bowl and a dinnerplate; a server filled the

bowl with what looked like vegetable soup. I was starving so I held my plate in front of everyone serving. I can't remember what I had to eat, but it tasted good. Once I finished eating, I dumped my plates in the hatch, which had a notice that read 'dirty plates'. I headed outside to wash my irons in the big galvanised washtub. The water was boiling hot and smelled horrible. I pitied anyone who dropped their irons into it, as they would definitely scald or burn their hands retrieving them.

A group of us walked back to G Lines together. Back at the billets, I had a look around my new home. The billets were made from wood and painted with black creosote; there was a big G and a number painted in white next to the entrance door. I could see that each billet was independent of each other and had a concrete path leading to its front door. Inside were two small rooms; one had a name on the door that read 'Corporal Brand'.

The other door said 'storeroom'. Inside were brushes, pans, rags, tins of polish and two weird-looking things with long handles that had heavy metal blocks attached to them. Next to the rags were two bundles of felt pads, which were just a little bigger than the bottom surface of the metal blocks. There were two bunches of yellow dusters next to the rags. Beyond the two rooms was a door that led into the main room. Eight beds were lined along each side of the room and in the middle were two Formica-topped tables and eight folding chairs. Waste bins were at the side of the tables and two ashtrays sat on each table top. Between each bed was a tall locker and a smaller locker. There were no pictures on the walls; our room looked bare and uninviting. The rear door led out to a series of corridors that had a workroom with a sink, two wooden tables and several ironing boards, each with an electric iron placed on a plate at the end of the board. There was a cupboard with cartons of Vim, scouring pads and disinfectant, and a few tins of Brasso.

Next came the toilets, the washbasins with mirrors above them, and the showers. Everything smelled of disinfectant and was spotlessly clean. I wandered up and down the corridors and soon realised that the billets were a mirror image of each other, just like a spider's web. I could see that in each room I passed, half the beds had been taken. Surveying my surroundings, I came to the conclusion I did not like where I'd ended up. I already regretted my choice and wished I was at home.

******

At precisely 13:30, over a hundred of us were lined up outside on the road. Standing in front of us was a sergeant and four corporals. All were dressed in blue trousers, and tunics that had flashes on the shoulders, which showed they were RAF regiment. There is only one regiment in the RAF. A blue/grey belt with gleaming brass buckles was around their waists and they all wore heavy boots that shined so much you could see your reflection in their toe-caps. Blue berets fitted neatly on their heads, pulled down over their right ears. A shiny badge with the initials RAF was fixed onto the side of each beret. The creases in their uniforms looked razor sharp.

"My name is Sergeant Coffee, and these gentlemen will be looking after you while you are here for your Initial Training Service. Remember their names. Corporal Benton." This person took a step forward and came to attention. "Corporal Brand, Corporal Rogerson and Corporal Edison." Each stepped forward when their name was called.

"All four corporals will live in one of the billet bunks while you are here. They will be teaching you about life as a boy entrant and will be responsible for your discipline while you are with us. This will be 12 weeks. You are the thirtieth entry of Boy Entrants and you will leave St Athan at the end of your training, which will be 18 months," Sgt Coffee barked. "You are now dismissed to enter your billets, where your corporals will teach you how to make your bed and keep your billet and ablutions clean."

We all broke lines and headed for our billet. A few minutes later, Corporal Brand came in through the front door. Those that were sitting, stood up. We were already becoming accustomed to the discipline in our new life. "I am Corporal Brand and I live in the bunk just through there."

Two minutes later, ten of us were standing in a group around a bed so that we could see Corporal Brand. He explained that more recruits would arrive later that afternoon and the next day. As we were the first to arrive, we were going to learn the ropes and it would be up to us to teach the others when they arrived. He took one of the blankets and folded it lengthwise into three. The other blankets and sheets were folded neatly and placed in order: blanket, sheet, blanket, sheet, blanket; and then he folded the first blanket neatly around this pile. Next, he showed us how to turn the pack over so that it lay on top of the small locker in a perfect box shape. He fitted the final blanket onto the mattress, folding the corners in what he called a 'hospital bed'. Finally, he placed the blankets and sheets, which he called the 'bed pack', onto the bed, so that no overlap showed. This was the task we had to practise until it was to the satisfaction of our corporal.

Once this was achieved, from the storeroom, Corporal Brand took three different sizes of brushes, a pan, a big, opened tin of polish, some rags, and the strange-looking implement with the heavy, cast-iron base. He placed these items neatly inside the entrance to the room. I thought that the light-brown linoleum was gleaming, but obviously that was not the corporal's opinion.

"Okay, listen up," he called, picking up the small brush. "This brush is used for sweeping up piles of dust." He picked up the next size brush and held it in front of his barrel chest. "This is not a brush. This is a broom, because it has a long handle and will be used for sweeping. A brush is an implement used for various purposes, including cleaning, painting, and brushing your hair. Remember this. Okay, you think this billet looks clean? I can assure you that it is filthy. Let me demonstrate."

With that, he swept an area of the floor, picking up nonexistent dust with the small brush and pan. He then placed a dollop of orange-coloured polish on the floor and rubbed it around the area with a rag, giving several of us a turn to do the same. He finally placed a felt pad on the floor and lifted the cast-iron block on top of it.

"This is called a 'bumper', and everyone takes turns at polishing the floor until it shines like a star. Don't worry if you wear a hole in the linoleum, we have plenty more!"

We all had a turn at 'swinging the bumper'. It was hard work. When we finished and had put away the brushes and bumper, he chatted and asked us friendly questions, such as where we were from and if any of us had any problems. I did not understand what he meant by problems - I just wanted to get out of the whole organisation.

I did not realise that perhaps this was the problem he had spoken about, being homesick and uncertain of my future. Other recruits started arriving and claiming their bed space. A very tall corporal and another much shorter one came in and chatted to Corporal Brand, who then told us to 'fall in' for our grand tour of the camp. Corporal Brand took one group, and Corporal Edison, the other. Corporal Edison was not quite as tall as me, looked no older than me, and he had a smooth baby face. Corporal Brand was rugged, stocky, and already had bristles on his chin.

Our first stop was the Navy Army and Air Force Institute, better known as the NAAFI. Here we could buy snacks, play table tennis and darts and watch TV. I had seen very little TV in my life and thought this would be great. There was also a NAAFI shop where you could buy essentials, such as stamps, writing pads, envelopes, cleaning materials for our uniform, and cigarettes.

Trying to stay in line, we passed Station Headquarters, referred to as SHQ. Facing SHQ was a huge tarmacked square, which looked to be about half a mile on each side. At one side of the square was a tall flagpole, and next to it, a smaller pole sticking out from the side where the RAF ensign was blowing in the breeze. A smaller flag fluttered from the very top of the pole. Corporal Brand warned us never to walk on the parade square unless it was an official drill or parade.

Following Corporal Brand, we arrived at the Young Men's Christian Association, commonly known as the YMCA; or simply, the YM. We could visit the YM, where the activities were similar to those at the NAAFI. Further on from the YM was the Astra Cinema, which Corporal Brand informed us was the name given to all cinemas on RAF stations.

Next to the Astra was a huge building. When inside, we could see that it was where we'd come for indoor sports. There was a large gymnasium with a raised boxing ring, benches, wall bars, a vaulting horse, parallel bars and weight training apparatus. Adjoining the gymnasium was an indoor five-a-side football pitch, and beyond that, a huge swimming pool. We saw several people wearing white T-shirts, thin black trousers and plimsolls. Corporal Brand told us that they were our physical education instructors. He told us that we were lucky because St Athan was home to the RAF Physical Training Instructor (PTI) School. Close by was the indoor drill parade ground, which was basically a converted aircraft hangar that doubled for indoor football and hockey.

On the way back to G Lines we passed a very tall landmark - a tower - which we were told was a water tower. The building next to it was the boiler house that pumped hot water through to the radiators in our billets. On reaching G Lines, we were advised to remain in our billets after we had eaten and to get a good night's sleep as we had to be standing by our beds at 08:00.

When I entered my billet, I could see that almost all the beds had bed packs on them. I guessed that the newcomers had been shown how to make them then gone to eat. I grabbed my irons and headed for the cookhouse. After a filling dinner, I was in my bed and asleep before 'lights out'.

******

Next morning, I was awake at 06:30. I really didn't have any choice, as the horn-shaped device fixed high in one of the corners of our billet blared out reveille. I washed, dressed, made up my bed pack, and was at breakfast eating my cereal and a good fry-up just after 07:00. On the way back to G Lines with some other new recruits, I saw a group of around ten young men in uniform coming towards us from the other side of the cookhouse. As they approached, I was thinking about tinned tomatoes, which I had just discovered I did not like. I thought they would say, 'Good morning' or something like that, and I was very surprised when they snarled at us like dogs. In unison, they growled, "Welcome sprogs," and continued to make rude and derogatory comments about us. No one in our group reacted to their behaviour and foul words. Later, I discovered that a 'sprog' is the term for a new recruit.

At precisely 08:00, Corporal Brand entered the billet and we stood to acknowledge him. He seemed to be a decent sort of person, not like the group we'd met on the way back from the cookhouse. He informed us that more recruits were arriving later that day, so we were going to be organised into smaller groups and escorted by one of the drill instructors to the Education Department. There, we would meet our Education Officers and Non-Commissioned Officers – NCOs – who would explain our training programme. The late arrivals had to remain in the billet while the rest fell in outside. We were divided into four groups of approximately thirty people. Corporal Kelloway was with Corporal Brand and it was he who addressed us.

"Okay, listen up!" Corporal Kelloway shouted. He then demonstrated the basic drill movements that we had to practise. I thought we did them rather well because he didn't shout or complain. When we arrived at the Education Department, we were dismissed and ushered into four separate rooms, which were set with tables and chairs.

Once we were all seated everyone was given a sheet of writing paper and a pen. It was official writing paper, as it was printed with the RAF St Athan address. We had to fill in our name and billet number in the relevant box. The information confirmed that the named boy entrant had arrived safely and was being cared for. His civilian clothing would be returned to the home address shown on the envelope after seven days. We were then told we could write a few words on the paper if we wanted. I wrote that I had arrived safely and had met up with some friends from Glasgow. I commented on the food, but said nothing about wanting to come home.

When we'd finished writing our letters, Corporal Kelloway, who was in charge of my group, asked everyone under sixteen years old to hold up their hand. I put mine in the air and he gave me another form to fill in. It was the 'permission to smoke' form, which stated that a boy entrant under sixteen years old had to have parental permission to smoke tobacco. There were then two lines of writing: one for giving permission and one for refusing permission, with a box at the side so that the relevant statement could be ticked. A further line stated that if permission was not received within two weeks, the named Boy Entrant could face disciplinary action if found smoking tobacco. After handing in the forms, we were given a smoke break. As the underage smoking rule was now official, I did not push my luck and stayed in the room.

Fifteen minutes later an officer, dressed smartly in a uniform with two rings at the bottom of the sleeves, entered the room. Instinctively, we all stood up.

"Good morning, please sit," were his first words. Our chairs scraped the floor as we sat again. On the blackboard he wrote 'Flight Lieutenant Williams' before turning to face us.

"Today, you will be in this classroom, but in future, during your education and training, you will be in smaller groups." My first thought was: 'Does that mean I'm going back to school? Surely not!'

"This morning, I am going to tell you a bit about your training here and what the future holds for you." With that he opened a drawer below one of the tables that were arranged around the walls and removed some posters. He hung one on two hooks in the wall at the side of the blackboard. I spent the next hour listening to his description of the RAF and the role of boy entrants.

CHAPTER 13

The Contract

I learned that the RAF Boy Entrant scheme started in the mid-1930s. Boys between the ages of 15 and 17 joined the RAF and underwent training in various occupations or trades, which prepared them for employment in the Royal Air Force. This type of training was suspended during World War II and recommenced in May 1947. There had been several changes since the scheme was introduced in the 1930s. When it became obvious that National Service would not be continued much longer, and that the RAF would have to maintain itself by voluntary recruitment, the recruitment of boy entrants was intensified so that they would become the backbone of the Royal Air Force's maintenance programmes. We were told that the Boy Entrant scheme involved 18 months of training and ran alongside an RAF apprentice scheme, which took between two and three years to complete. If anyone on the Boy Entrant scheme proved worthy, they could transfer to the apprentice scheme. When we graduated, we would probably be posted to Bomber Command or Fighter Command. Those of us who were lucky enough to graduate would be maintaining some of the most up-to-date fighter aircraft in the world or maintaining our bombers - including our 'V' Force.

Flight Lieutenant Williams said, "Let me explain your terms of service," as he changed the poster that was hanging up. "In 1952, Boy Entry applicants aged 15 to 17 were required to enter into a contract with the Air Ministry, which required the successful candidate to serve a minimum of ten years. This was effective when he reached the age of 18, plus two years in the reserve service. At the end of the ten years, they were discharged with one month's pay. The service terms have now been altered to nine years' service, plus three years in the reserve, and one month's severance pay. This is the contract you have signed."

He added that we could later have the chance to extend our service to twelve years or twenty-two years. The difference between these two periods of time was crucial – if we signed up for twenty-two years we would get a pension. Talk of pensions held little or no interest to 15 and 16 year olds, but his next words made our ears prick up.

"Now, let me tell you about your pay."

I thought, 'That's what I want to hear about.'

I was soon brought down to earth when he said, "All you are entitled to is one shilling."

One boy blurted out, "Only a shilling! That's not much for nine years' work."

The Flight Lieutenant looked at him, smiled and said, "That's what you are entitled to, because tomorrow you're required to swear an Oath of Allegiance to our queen, and that is what entitles you to a shilling. However, you will also be paid a weekly sum of approximately three pounds by the Government. You choose how this money is used. You may wish to send some of this money home and you will be required to open a Post Office Savings Account. You will then be given, from the remaining balance, enough money – not the total amount that is left – to buy what you need while you are here. The rest will be saved for you and given back when you complete your initial training and go home on leave."

I thought that three pounds, as well as free food and lodgings, sounded like a fortune – this must be what was meant by leaving home to seek your fortune. I thought about my father, who was paid just over seven pounds a week to provide for Lizzie and my three sisters. So much information was being rolled out to us, I could see that everyone was ready for the smoke break.

An extract from the regulations covering Pay and Conditions of Service at that time is shown in Appendix 2.

Back in the classroom, Flight Lieutenant Williams explained that, "thanks to the RAF's experience with aptitude and intelligence tests, and the knowledge that a lack of education did not mean a lack of intelligence, the RAF has been able to train suitable candidates in the appropriate trades to create the backbone of the RAF's technical services."

He looked straight at us and said, "You must remember that you are also part of Great Britain's military machine and, if necessary, you could be required to fight, just like any soldier.

"You will be trained in the requirements of military discipline, fitness of the body, and the operational use and maintenance of firearms and other weapons - namely rifles with fixed bayonets, machine guns (Bren and STEN guns) and hand-grenades."

I looked at him wondering what he was going to say next.

He smiled and added, "As the RAF don't employ servants or cleaners, you will be responsible for keeping your billets and work areas clean."

I had already experienced the cleaning part and did not fancy it. I thought to myself, 'I could be going to war, just like in the movies.'

He looked at us seriously and said, "If you do wrong, you will soon become familiar with the term 'punishment'. Enough about that. That will happen if you don't use your brains properly. My job will be to educate you and prepare you for your next stage of training."

With that ringing in my ears, we were dismissed. We lined up outside and marched back to our billets to get our irons before lunch. At least, I thought it was marching. I noticed that when I entered the billet there were signs more recruits had arrived.

On our return to the classroom, we found that we had a new teacher. He introduced himself as Chief Technician

Turner, and he told us to address him as 'Chief'. A hand went up and a boy asked, "Chief, why are your stripes upside down?"

Chief replied, "Because I am a maintenance technician, which is what you will eventually become. Your promotion will depend on you passing exams and practical tests, not on discipline and fighting skills. When you see an airman with upside-down stripes, it means that they are technical people. Then, if you pass the tests and kept your nose clean, you could become a Chief Technician after about fifteen years."

This sounded like a good prospect to me, but at that moment I couldn't see myself spending fifteen years in the RAF.

We spent the rest of the day learning about St Athan, recognising different ranks, what to do when the flag was hoisted, and who was who in the chain of command.

******

Before he left us at our billet, Corporal Kelloway told us to be out on the road in our groups at 08:00 next morning because it was an important day.

"Tomorrow, you will be required to swear the Oath of Allegiance, and then you will be fully inducted as a boy entrant."

He advised us to get an early night as the following day would be a tough one. I couldn't sleep as I had so much going on in my brain. I was thinking, 'What am I going to do, I don't want to be here anymore.' By the sounds of restlessness in the billet, I guessed I wasn't the only one who wanted to go home.

Next morning, I was back in the classroom by 08:30. Just before 09:00, my group stood to attention when a squadron leader entered the room. He introduced himself as Squadron Leader Harkness then wrote his name on the blackboard. He explained again the purpose of the oath and our one-shilling entitlement. He asked us if there were any Catholics in the group and no one raised a hand. A Bible was then placed in front of each recruit. At this point, he paused and looked at us intently before saying, "If anyone does not wish to take the oath then they should leave the room now. You will be given a rail ticket and expenses to cover your journey home."

He paused again. There was a tense silence in the room. This was such an important decision and I was shaking all over. My fear of the future made me want to leave the room. I still did not know if this was the right thing to do. I sensed that there were others in the room who felt the same as me. But no one moved.

After a few moments we were asked to stand up. Squadron Leader Harkness looked straight ahead, and with a serious look on his face said, "Remove the printed card from the Bible and hold the Bible in your right hand."

I did as I was told. I was still shaking.

He continued, "While holding the Bible in your right hand and the card in your left hand, when I give you the signal to do so I want you all to read the words on the card, saying your full name when you reach the dotted line. Do you all understand?"

He looked straight at us and I stared straight back at him. He reminded me of a hangman about to put the hood over my head. My knees started to wobble. I said to myself over and over, "It's too bloody late now, just get on with it."

No one spoke and he signalled to start. Squeezing the Bible as hard as I could, I read these words from the card:

RAF Form 60

OATH TO BE TAKEN BY RECRUIT ON ATTESTATION

I, ------------------------, swear by almighty God that I will be faithful and bear true allegiance to Her Majesty Queen Elizabeth the Second, Her Heirs and Successors, and that I will, as in duty bound, honestly and faithfully defend her Majesty, Her Heirs and Successors, in person, Crown and Dignity against all enemies, and will observe and obey all orders of Her Majesty, Her Heirs and Successors, and of the Air Officers and Officers set over me. So help me God.

When we had finished, my mind felt empty. The only thing I could think of was, 'What have I done?' I hardly heard Squadron Leader Harkness congratulating us on becoming the 30th Entry to the Royal Air Force Boy Entrant Service. He handed us over to Corporal Kelloway, who said, "Anybody who smokes can leave the room for a ten-minute break."

Everyone left the room. Outside, the conversation centred around the same question, "Have I done the right thing?" Everyone was tense. Permission or no permission, almost everyone lit up, including me.

Once back inside, Corporal Kelloway issued us new recruits with a blue card that had the word 'arrivals' on the left-hand side and 'departures' on the right. We were instructed to fill in our full name and nothing else. I could see that there were people with boxes and papers filing through the corridor outside. I guessed that now was paperwork time.

When my name was called, an orderly stamped a number next to my name, which was also printed on a separate card. He told me to keep the card safe as this was my temporary 1250 ID card. I looked at my number: 1933687.

CHAPTER 14

Tailored Suits and a New Hairstyle

Next morning, I was up at reveille: washed, dressed, bed pack made up, bed space swept, and ready to go ten minutes before we were due to fall in outside. During the night, I thought I had heard someone sobbing in a bed close to mine. The boy on the left of me had introduced himself as Squeak Thomson. He had been given that nickname because his voice had not yet broken. I thought that it could have been Squeak who had been sobbing, but I was not certain. Maybe I had been asleep and dreamt that I had heard sobbing. I think I was also dreaming that my life couldn't get any worse. When I woke up I found out that I was wrong. It was going to get a lot worse.

"Right, you scruffy lot!" was the first thing Sergeant Coffee bellowed out. The second was, "Listen up! Today, you'll learn what it's like to be a boy entrant. You're going to learn drill manoeuvres. We can't have you walking around like a load of pansies. Your hair will be cut. We don't want you looking like a load of girls. Today, you'll be issued with a uniform. We can't have you walking around like a load of teddy boys, can we?" He looked directly at a boy in the front rank. "And to make sure you all know how to keep your billets clean and tidy, you will clean and polish G Lines until they are fit for my inspection tomorrow morning. Any skivers will find themselves on a charge - they may find they're in the cookhouse scrubbing pans for the next twelve weeks!"

That was the first time I had heard the word 'skiver'. I didn't relish the thought of scrubbing pans.

"Right!" he screamed. "Let's get to it, chop, chop. Corporal Edison, march your lot to the barber shop. Corporal

Kelloway, get your lot inside and start cleaning. Corporal Brand, show your lot how basic drill movements should be performed." With that, Sergeant Coffee headed in the direction of headquarters.

We practiced basic drill movements, coming to attention, right and left turn, right dress and open order. I could tell from the bawling and shouting, plus the sarcastic remarks from our drill instructors, the DIs, that we were never going to get it right, even though the movements were straightforward. Thankfully, my group was next for the barber shop.

There were three barbers, and when my turn came I sat in the chair and accepted my fate. Two minutes later, I had my short back and sides and had joined the others outside for a smoke. I was freezing.

Less than an hour later, we were marched to the quartermaster's store to collect our kit and to be measured for our uniforms. As we entered the store, which was essentially a big warehouse, an orderly gave each of us two sheets of paper on which was printed all our kit items. The first item was a canvas kit bag that everything else went in. The orderly asked what my shoe size was; he then produced two pairs of size nine boots and two pairs of black shoelaces, which he placed in the kit bag.

As we filed around the counters, the storemen read out the item they were giving out. I was supposed to check each item off on the sheets of paper, but this was impossible because of the speed the kit was issued. When my kit bag was almost full I finally arrived at the end counter. Another orderly gave me a pen and I had to sign the bottom of both sheets and hand them back. I asked him if I could have two more sheets so that I could learn the names of the items. "Good thinking," he said, giving me two more sheets.

Lugging the kit bag so that it made minimum contact with the floor, I reached the tailor's shop. There were three civilian tailors. The first one measured my waist, inside leg, chest and head before shouting out two numbers. An orderly produced two uniforms, a beret and a service dress hat. The orderly said, "The last item is an SD cap. Don't put it in your kit bag. Wear it, so that it won't get damaged."

The next two tailors checked that our uniforms fitted properly. We took it in turns to go behind a curtain to change into them. If any adjustments were needed, they marked them with tailor's chalk, wrote out a card and fixed half the card to the item, giving the other half to the boy entrant. I was lucky as I did not need any adjustments, so I folded my uniforms neatly and put them into my kit bag. The bag was full, so when I was given my final item - my service greatcoat - I had to carry it over my arm while I carried my kit bag on my left shoulder. By the time we marched back to G Lines it was almost lunchtime. I was worn out, starving and cursing the man in the hat who had persuaded me to join up.

****

My day went further downhill. At 13:00 Sergeant Coffee and his four DIs lined up in front of us.

"Right, corporals, let me see what they can do." With that, each DI put us through the basic drill movements. When we were instructed to 'stand at ease' I suspected that Sergeant Coffee was not a happy man. He bawled and screamed at us for being the worst shambles he had ever seen, and that, if there was not a vast improvement we would all be on the parade square until 22:00.

"Now, listen up! You poor excuses for boy entrants!" he shouted. "You'll have seen your mothers sewing and using irons to press clothes. Well, listen up, that's what you're going to be doing for the rest of the day. Corporals, get this shambles out of my sight!" With that he turned and headed in the direction of his office.

Corporal Edison took over and called everyone to attention. With a sneer on his face, he roared, "Everyone, get inside. Stand by your beds with your kit bags. Dismissed!" We turned to the right and headed for our billets.

It had been one of the worst days of my life and it wasn't going to improve.

Corporal Brand came in and we stood at attention with our kit bag at our left side. When he called out to stand easy I felt relieved. His attitude seemed a bit more relaxed as he started to teach us the names of the items in our kit, how we should lay them out in our lockers, and how to lay our kit out on the bed for inspection. When he came to the two packets that held our badges, flashes and hatbands, he held up a small canvas bag.

"This is your housewife," he said as he opened it out. Inside there were needles, threads, a thimble, a small pair of scissors, spare buttons, some wool for darning our socks, plus a few other bits and pieces that I did not recognise. He handed out some diagrams that showed us where we had to position our badges and instructions on how to fix them to our hats and sleeves. He took a chequered band and demonstrated how to fit it around our SD cap and how to fit the identification discs behind the cap badges. It looked straightforward enough.

His next instruction shocked me. He told us to get sewing, as he expected to see us standing by our beds at 08:00, correctly dressed in our work uniforms, which he called 'work blues' or 'battle dress'. He added that those who had items to collect from the tailor would wear their denims - their work overalls - over their shirts. After the drill, the instructions and all the shouting, I was tired and hungry, so I was relieved that. after a demonstration of how to iron, he left the billet.

Automatically, we hung our uniforms on the metal coat hangers in the tall locker. Dai Hughes called out, "Can I make a suggestion? We're going to be at this all night unless we work together. Why don't this side of the room go to dinner while the other side starts ironing the clothes and when you guys come back, we will go to dinner."

Ken Langley chipped in, "I know how to iron, I'll start with the ironing. I'll do the shirts first and move on to the uniforms later. If someone is good at sewing, they can sew my flashes and badges on."

We all agreed and I headed to the cookhouse. When I returned, my shirts were folded neatly on my bed. I went in to the ironing room and took over from Ken who showed me once more what to do before he went for his meal.

By 20:00 we were making good progress. That was when Corporal Brand, dressed in civilian clothes, entered the billet. He quickly realised that we had a team plan in action, but made no comment. Before he left he told us he was going out that night and would be back late. No one asked him what time that would be, but we knew that official 'lights out' was 22:00. We made it! All our shirts and uniforms had been pressed and looked perfect. We had used old pillowcases from the store room, wet them, and used them to get perfect creases with no burn marks on the uniforms.

******

As soon as reveille sounded I got up, and was one of the first in the queue for breakfast. At 07:15 I was trying to fix a collar onto the collar stud that I'd managed to fit into the hole on the back of my new shirt. At 07:50 I had swept my bed space and taken my turn to bumper the floor, ready for Sergeant Coffee's inspection. I learned why there were so many felt pads in the storeroom – we moved like ice skaters, sliding around on the felt pads, to protect our highly-polished floor. At least we thought it was polished, but Corporal Brand had other ideas.

He walked up and down, making derogative comments. Finally, he stood at the bottom door and commented, "Your billet will be inspected in around ten minutes. I suggest you use the time wisely." With that he walked out.

A few minutes later, I heard him shouting at someone to get out of the toilets. "Come on, boy, chop, chop. I don't want to see your arse when I'm inspecting the latrines." I heard the clatter of the boy's boots as he ran down the wooden corridor.

Twenty minutes later, it was our turn for inspection. Corporal Brand followed behind as Sergeant Coffee stood in front of each person, eyeing up their uniform and bed. When he got to Squeak, he bawled out, "Boy, you look like a rag doll! After inspection, get back to the tailor shop and get your uniform fixed. Straight after that report to the dental centre where you will join your squad for a dental examination."

Next, he turned to Squeak's bed pack and dumped it on the floor. "Your bed pack looks worse than your trousers. Remake it." Soon there were four other bed packs and a number of kit items on the floor. "Thank you, Corporal Brand!" he hollered, turning to leave the room for the next billet. Before he did so, he added, "I'll be back in ten minutes. Make sure that corrections are done. Dismissed."

Some of the others helped to make up the offending bed packs and tidy up. I grabbed the bumper and got swinging. After the stipulated time the corporal returned and told us that our billet was one of the worst in the whole of G Lines. He had a pile of cloth bags in his hand.

"Now, listen up," he growled. "These are laundry bags. Put your civilian clothes in one of these bags and write your name on the label, then put the bags in the corridor so that they can be collected. We don't want your parents to see skid-marks on your drawers, do we? Right, outside in ten minutes! Those of you that need to go back to the tailor can go as soon as you've done your laundry."

******

After inspection we were marched to the dental section where I had to wait my turn to be subjected to a teeth and gum inspection, which was recorded on a dental chart. I was told to make an appointment with the hygienist. Most of the boys were told the same thing, though a few had to make appointments with the dentist.

The medical centre was the next stop, where I went through the same routine that I'd been subjected to at Cosford, only this time it was a more detailed examination and the results were recorded on a medical chart. Finally, I was inoculated against typhoid and tetanus: a TABT jab. By the time we were all inoculated, there were some very sick-looking boys and I had a painful arm. These inspections took up most of the day. When we returned to our billets I had to prepare for the 'best blue' inspection the following morning. Another inspection!

I think the majority of us were ready to give up and run away; fortunately, we were bonding as a team. We talked amongst ourselves and got acquainted with boys from the other billets. We laughed and joked about our superiors and made up suitable nicknames for our DIs. Sergeant Coffee was 'Chop Chop'; Corporal Edison was 'Baby Face' and Corporal Kelloway was 'Stretch'. Corporal Brand wasn't given a nickname because, so far, he'd seemed okay – he'd not been an obnoxious, loud bully like every other DI. Everyone agreed that Baby Face Edison needed castrating.

Corporal Brand soon showed his true colours the next morning when we stood to attention in our 'best blue'. He closely inspected our uniforms and the billet before Sergeant Coffee arrived. Then he began to tear us apart.

"You're the worst souls I've ever been in charge of!" he yelled. "Your best blues look like you've slept in them. As for your bed packs…they're sagging in the middle and look more round than square. And your beds – your hospital corners are more like hospital dinners, and your SD caps look like NAFFI doughnuts. Get yourselves smartened up!"

When he paused for breath, I heard Sergeant Coffee's boots stamping up the corridor. 'What the hell can we do right?' I asked myself, and I realised that the answer was nothing.

I had survived for four days. I was looking forward to a rest from the onslaught. I mistakenly thought that Saturday and Sunday would consist of two days' rest and recuperation. I had visions of going to the local town, to visit the cinema or perhaps enjoying a game of football. No such luck; Sergeant Coffee had other ideas.

After performing two hours of drill movements, which Sergeant Coffee thought were worse than the day we arrived, he gave us the bad news. On Saturday morning there would be an inspection by the flight commander. That sounded serious to me. He reeled off a list of things that we had to do like he was firing a machine gun:

Our kit had to be laid out on our beds in regulatory fashion

Ablutions had to be spotless. I had learned this meant the toilets, washbasins, showers, etc.

The floor, buttons and our boots had to be polished until you could see your reflection in them

"I hope I make myself clear! When you're dismissed you'll return to your billets where you'll be given brown paper, string and pens. Fold your civilian clothes neatly and make a parcel to send them back to your home address. Anyone failing to come up to the required standard will face disciplinary action."

Needless to say, those words echoed in my ears when I was dismissed.

"Come on, chop, chop!" Sergeant Coffee ordered. A short while after this tirade, Corporal Brand entered the room and we all jumped to attention. We must have looked ridiculous as we were standing on felt pads. He had a large bag of cloth labels for which he gave instructions – no item of clothing had to go in the laundry bag unless it was labelled clearly with the first three letters of our name and the last three numbers of our identity number, marked clearly in indelible ink.

"Right, listen up!" he snarled. "I'll be popping in from time to time to make sure none of you are practising Egyptian PT."

"What's Egyptian PT?" Dai asked.

"Lying in your pit!" retorted Corporal Brand as he headed for the door. I felt sick. I'd had enough of all this bullshit. I was ready to explode, but I knew that would be stupid - I'd only face more bullshit. Instead, to ease my tension, I lit up a Woodbine and just got on with it.

******

The highlight of my day was when Jimmy Laurie, my

friend from Glasgow, and Mike Robertson, my friend from the Shetland Islands, walked through the door. Jimmy had been delayed due to a family funeral, and Mike had been delayed because of bad weather. I was so happy to see them both. From the moment we'd met, we had gelled; we'd stuck together through stressful times at the recruitment centre until I left the train at Carlisle on my return from Cosford. We'd be able to help one another again, but only from a distance as, unfortunately, they were housed in a different billet to me and would be in a different flight, which meant I would not see them during the day. It would be good to see them in our free time in the NAAFI, however, to swap our tales of woe or success, if such a moment ever occurred.

The only break I got on Friday was after dinner, when I went to the NAAFI to buy some cigarettes and more Duraglit. The tin Corporal Brand had donated was not enough for everyone. The NAAFI was empty except for a few people buying chocolate because they'd missed dinner, and cigarettes for during breaks; and, of course, the essential Duraglit. Thankfully, we'd been given enough polish and Blanco with our first issue when we arrived; otherwise, I could see that most of my pay would be spent on cleaning materials for my uniform.

I worked right through until the lights went out at 22:00. I don't think anyone was still asleep when reveille sounded at 06:30, as our body clocks had begun to respond to the routine. At 07:00, I was in the first shift to go to breakfast, but I was back for my slot on the bumper by 07:20. The flight commander's inspection was to start at 09:00, which did not leave much time to prepare.

Flight Lieutenant Day arrived at exactly 09:00. I was beginning to realise how important timing, precision and perfection were in the RAF. The inspection did not take as long as I thought it would and I did not hear any screaming or shouting from up the corridor. When Flight Lieutenant Day entered G6, Corporal Brand called out, "Officer present," and we all stood to attention. Corporal Brand saluted Flight

Lieutenant Day, who returned the salute and instructed us to, "Stand at ease." As the flight lieutenant approached each bed, in turn, the respective boy came to attention; he'd call out his name and state the last three digits of his service number. By the time he reached my bed space I'd heard these words twice, "Sergeant, make a note." Then came a reason, which I found unintelligible. When it came to my turn I could see the morning sun streaming through the window of the bed space opposite me; the air seemed to be full of dust particles. When the flight lieutenant was directly in front of me, I came to attention. I looked straight forward and called out, "Carruthers 687, sir." His only words were, "Sergeant, make a note. This man has dust in his bed space."

It was the first time I'd taken a good look at Flight Lieutenant Day. He was slightly taller than me and a little overweight. He had a moustache and looked to be about the same age as my father. I said nothing in reply to his comments as he walked on to the next bed space. I stood at ease, but I was not at ease as I imagined some of the worst things I could do to him. How was I supposed to stop the sun shining and revealing dust particles in its rays? I felt that his reprimand was totally unjustified. As he left, Corporal Brand called us to attention and saluted. He gave the order for us to stand easy and stay in the room. The wait seemed endless. What punishment would I get? I felt that too many of us had failed the inspection. Nothing positive had been said to us since our arrival, so I did not expect good news.

Corporal Brand returned an hour later with a smirk on his face. "Well done," he smiled. "Only three of you got picked up on inspection. Right, listen up!" I was fed up of hearing that phrase, but gave him my attention anyway. "First, the three people that were not up to standard will fall in outside at 18:00 hrs, wearing their denims, to be ready for fatigue duty."

I thought he was going to say 'listen up' again, but he didn't. Instead, he offered good news. "This afternoon you're free to go to the NAAFI, the YM, the cinema, the gym or just walk around the camp. You are confined to East Camp and not permitted on any main road or to enter any official building. Is that clear?"

In unison, we answered, "Yes, corporal."

"A word of warning. You are likely to meet other boy entrants and regular airmen, NCOs or officers. If you meet an officer, what should you do, Green?"

Cliff Green replied, "Salute him, corporal."

"And if he is walking past, what do you do, Dickson?"

"Eyes right or left and salute him, corporal."

"Okay, if you meet another boy entrant with stripes on their arm, what do you do, Carruthers?"

"Treat them like any NCO, corporal," I replied.

"Good, because remember you are the junior entry and, if a 'sergeant boy' places you on a charge, you will be in deep trouble."

Just then a boy entered the room and told Corporal Brand that the post office van had come to collect our parcels. I felt like crying when I gave my parcel of clothes to the postman. Corporal Brand waited until all our personal possessions had been taken to the van.

"Right, listen up!" I could not believe he had more orders for us. "Tomorrow, you will be outside at 09:30 dressed in your best blue with shining boots for church parade. Right, then, enjoy your afternoon."

As I came to attention I thought, 'Enjoy my afternoon? Not much chance of that.'

CHAPTER 15

School with a Difference

When I ventured out with some of the boys from my billet, I was surprised to find so few people around. I opened the gym door to have a boy who was dressed in shorts, shirt and plimsolls shout, "No boots allowed." I quickly closed the door, though I'd had enough time to see that it was quite busy. We did not enter the pool area for fear we would get into trouble.

As we walked about we encountered several boys senior to us who took great pleasure in making snide remarks. Nobody had a friendly word at all. We agreed that enough was enough and decided to head for our NAAFI. ITS boys had their own NAAFI, which is why we thought we'd be safe from orders and negative comments there. As we approached the NAAFI two boys with a single upside-down stripe at the bottom of each sleeve approached us. We had learned enough by now to know that they were not the most senior entry. Cliff Green, the biggest lad in our group, quietly said, "Any snide remarks and I'll hit them."

No one had time to reply to Cliff's remark before one of the two boys spoke. He pleasantly asked us if we were from the 30th Entry. I could sense that Cliff was gunning for a showdown, but their attitude was quite friendly so I relaxed a bit. They asked where we were from. The weather had turned colder and we were freezing. Gus suggested that if we bought the two boys a cup of tea and a doughnut they may give us some tips on how to survive in ITS. I felt that we had met, for the first time in this accursed place, actual human beings, so I quickly agreed. We all went inside and some of our entry looked up in shock as we sat down at a table with the two boys more senior to us. Cliff and I ordered mugs of tea and a plate of doughnuts and we shared the cost.

The first discussion centred around the DIs. We already knew they were all bastards, but we were a bit surprised when Gus told us that Corporal Brand and Sergeant Coffee were actually okay, and that we would come to appreciate them as we went through our training. Gus and the other boy, Archie, gave us tips on which Boy NCOs, PTIs, and education officers to watch out for and avoid, if possible. They gave us tips on bulling our boots and laying out our kit. We were advised to go to the early show at the cinema, and to avoid the late show; also, to never sit in the back rows where the visiting girls sat with the senior entry. I said that I had been put on fatigues and asked what that meant.

Gus said, "Don't worry, everybody gets fatigues because they need people to clean the cookhouse pots and do other cleaning jobs around the camp. Your orderly corporal will escort you to wherever they want you to clean. It's usually the cookhouse to start with. The good thing is you get tea and cake when you finish cleaning."

Cliff asked, "Why is it that the tea in the cookhouse tastes funny?" Gus replied that they put bromide in the tea to stop us getting a 'hard on'.

We all laughed at this ploy and wondered if it would work on us. Gus looked worried and said, "We need to go now, we don't want anyone to see that we're fraternising with sprogs." We thanked them and checked the road was clear for them to leave.

At 18:00, around 30 defaulters, myself included, marched to the cookhouse. Ten of us washed pots, swept and mopped floors - doing every dirty job that the catering staff did not like doing. The other twenty were scattered around doing other tasks no one wanted to do. Two-and-a-half hours later I was sweating and felt ill because of the hard work and the smell of the pots. When I finished, though, I still managed to tuck into a slice of Madeira cake and a mug of tea, despite the aroma of bromide.

It soon became apparent that ITS recruits would not be

placed under the disciplinary procedure of being charged with an offence. Our DIs would be responsible for discipline. They had the authority to place a boy on fatigue duty at any time they felt standards were not being met. As we were never going to come up to their pinnacle of excellence, there was a continuous stream of people doing fatigues every night.

******

Breakfast on Sunday started an hour later, but that did not mean a lie-in. There was always something that needed doing to keep our uniforms and billet in a state of gleaming perfection. Bulling my boots was the most difficult task, but I was lucky because I followed Gus's advice. I used a hot spoon to remove the baubles, followed by spit and polish. It was hard work and took several hours. As I prepared for church parade, I looked down at my boots and was proud of the way they gleamed.

When we had fallen in, Corporal Edison brought us to attention and called 'open order' then 'right dress'. He followed Sergeant Coffee around during his inspection. Almost all the sergeant's complaints related to dirty boots, dirty buttons and scruffy appearance. When he passed me, his only complaint was that my buttons were ingrained with remains of Duraglit.

Once his scrutiny was over, Sergeant Coffee informed us that we had two choices. The only choice I'd had up to that point was the food I wanted on my plate.

"Right, listen up!" he ordered. "As you cannot be forced to attend church, your choices are…one: attend the church service voluntarily. Two: march to the indoor parade ground for one hour's drill." Naturally, the church was full.

On our return to G Lines, Sergeant Coffee, with his usual repartee - 'Now, listen up' - advised us that, from the following day, our training would begin in earnest. We would be given a timetable for the first month. This cheered me up a bit as I felt I'd be learning something interesting –

not just the best way to shine floors and make the perfect bed pack. I spent the rest of the afternoon working on my boots and buttons. I was determined to beat the system! I hated scrubbing pans. At 18:00, along with others who had failed the flight commander's inspection, I fell in for fatigue duty.

Next morning, we were expected to be on parade at 08:30, which meant I had to fall in on the road outside five minutes before the DIs arrived. We were divided into four separate groups, called flights. I was in No. 2 Flight with around 70 others. Corporal Brand was nominated as my DI. After another inspection by Sergeant Coffee our timetable was called out. The day would be divided into two periods: from 08.00 until 12.00 and from 13.00 until 16:30. My work day would be devoted to drill, physical education (PEd), ground defence training (GDT) and continuing education (CE). I thought that I would enjoy physical education the best.

The four DIs were ordered to begin the programme with a drill. This time, we did not practise on the road, but marched to the square instead. Although there were four separate groups, you focused on your own DI's commands. We marched around the square for two hours, swinging our arms to shoulder height, coming to a halt, performing right turns, left turns, about turn, open order, right dress and other commands. As the morning progressed, my feet felt as if they were on fire. Thankfully, we were given a twenty-minute break, within which I'd have loved to plunge my feet into cold water, but a smoke break had to suffice. Smoking was not permitted on the square, so we were marched to the YM or NAAFI.

Marching had given me cramp and it was quite painful. I was fit from playing football and running, but not for hours of marching, which punished my body. Corporal Brand had called my flight every derogative name he knew, stopping short of calling us 'bastards', and not using the 'F' and 'C' swear-words. It was frowned upon for DIs to use those words - and if any boy entrant was heard uttering them he'd get seven days' punishment. I was so relieved when we finally marched back to G Lines. My legs felt like lead weights and I had a burning sensation in my feet.

Promptly, at 13:00, we marched to the building that housed the gymnasium. Inside, we were met by four physical training instructors (PTIs), a sergeant and three corporals. Within a minute of our DIs handing us over, the sergeant PTI screamed threats and abuse at us. He started with, "Right, you lot," and I was sure he would say the obligatory 'Now, listen up', but he didn't. He yelled, "You are poor excuses for men, but exercise will sort that out!"

My group started with a cross-country run, while the other two groups began in the gymnasium and the indoor parade ground, which doubled as a running track and five-a-side football pitch. Another two PTIs joined my flight for the run. On our return to start circuit training, more PTIs arrived to put their trainees through the pain barrier. When we finally stopped for a break, I felt like I'd run a marathon. My body felt numb and my brain could only think about food and the cookhouse.

The rest of the week followed a similar pattern: drill and PEd. Most of the PEd consisted of cross country running and circuit training, but there were a few enjoyable times when we played five-a-side football or indoor hockey. Those who wanted swimming lessons were told to buy a pair of swimming trunks from the NAAFI shop.

******

The best moment that week was when Corporal Brand told us that, on Thursday afternoon, we would have 'pay parade'. That day, we marched – we marched everywhere – to the indoor parade ground and were brought to a halt in front of two tables. An officer sat behind each one and an orderly stood at his side. On each table were sheets of paper, pens and a large money box. Each DI brought their flight to a halt and we left turned to face the tables. Next came the order to right dress and stand at ease.

The procedure was straightforward. When my name was

called, I had to come to attention, march to the table, come to a halt, salute, state my name and the last three digits of my service number, and place my temporary identification card on the table. Names were called in alphabetical order, so I was one of the first to go up and receive my pay. I followed the correct procedure and marched smartly to the table when my name was called. The orderly checked my name against my temporary ID card and read, "Carruthers, two shillings and sixpence." I almost died with shock. I stared at the half-crown coin on the table in front of me. I felt like asking 'Is that all I get?' However, I knew better than to question the regime in which I now lived. I picked up the offending coin and my ID card, saluted, about turned, and marched back to the space I'd vacated. I felt worthless. All that pain for such a measly reward. Would it last me the week and keep me in cigarettes and chocolate treats? I doubted it very much – most would probably go on Duraglit and boot polish.

All pain and no gain. My thoughts turned to home – I wished I was there. I felt low; a puny half-crown in return for over a week of torture. Friday had been the worst day for drill. The DIs shouted and screamed interminably with a succession of derogatory remarks.

"You're the worst bunch of recruits that has ever lived!" "You don't know your left feet from your right!" "You're a shower of misfits!"

The PTIs were no better, as they strived to make us feel like we were a bunch of freaks that had never done a day's exercise in our lives. The only consolation was that I did not get fatigues after the flight commander's inspection, and I also enjoyed the church service on Sunday.

Corporal Brand told us that, on Monday, we'd start our next phase of training, which would involve re-educating us.

Finally, came a chance to relax. On Saturday afternoon a group of us went to the matinee at the Astra Cinema. 'The Searchers', starring John Wayne, was showing and I really enjoyed the film. The cinema was not full, and I noticed that it was only the lower entries that were there. The weekend passed without hassle from figures of authority.

******

I was apprehensive on Monday morning when we came to a halt and right turned in the road in front of the education centre - a complex of huts and offices, similar to our accommodation in G Lines. A smartly-dressed airman, with three stripes and a crown, carrying several sheets of paper, stood outside the entrance waiting for us to arrive. After speaking with Corporal Edison he turned to face us and said, "Right, lads, stand easy and pay attention. We have got a lot to get through and the quicker we do it the quicker you get into a warm classroom."

Corporal Edison looked sick as he listened to the easy, friendly tones of the senior NCO.

"I am Chief Technician Turner and I will be one of your instructors. You can address me as 'chief'. He read out the classrooms, and the names of who was to file into each room. I found the classroom easily when my name was announced. I felt a lot happier. It was great to see Baby Face Edison squirm, even though I knew he'd take it out on us later. Once inside the classroom I felt relaxed. It was a typical classroom, like those in my old school, Annan Academy. The only difference was that there were tables with drawers, rather than desks. Everything else was familiar: a blackboard, chalk, posters and a store cupboard. I selected a table on the left of the room and sat down on the wooden chair.

A few minutes later an officer entered the room and we all stood to attention. He was a tall, lean man around fifty years old. He had a grey bushy moustache and he wore an immaculate uniform not unlike our best blue. He wasn't wearing a hat.

"Sit down," he ordered, "and remove your hats."

I took off my beret and placed it neatly in the drawer. I couldn't believe it - I'd joined the RAF to escape school and here I was, back in school!

"My name is Squadron Leader Evans." He'd written his

name in the top right-hand corner of the blackboard. In a resonating voice, that those at the back of the room could clearly hear, he said, "Welcome to St Athan Education Centre."

I looked around and counted fifteen students. Our teacher had a register in front of him; he started to call out our names, to which we replied 'sir' when our name was called.

With a huge smile on his face he stood up and said, "Relax. This is not like the previous school you attended. I will tell you the difference. You already have a basic understanding of English, maths and science. What we are going to do is to build on those basic skills so that you become skilled tradesmen. First, you will learn about the RAF, its structure, the organisation and history." For the first time I began to feel proud of myself and the decision I'd made to join up.

"Secondly, you are going to be maintenance technicians; therefore, you need to know what makes an aeroplane fly and stay in the air. I will teach you the theory of flight." He paused again to let this information sink in.

"Thirdly, because you gentlemen are going to be electrical tradesmen, you need to know about the electrical equipment on an aircraft and how it works. A colleague will teach you the theory of electricity, and then you will move into the workshops to carry out maintenance."

Looking around the room to make sure he had everyone's attention, he added, "Finally, you need to be competent and confident in the English language." I gave a little sigh and my confidence plummeted.

"Don't worry, it's not the kind of English you'll have done in the past. The English you will learn will be concerned with the administration that a large organisation like the RAF uses to maintain a high level of organisational excellence. You will become familiar with the forms that are used and learn how to fill them in. You will also be taught how to write reports and how to present them."

Squadron Leader Evans paused and smiled, "You might even learn enough English so that the Scots, English, Irish and Welsh can understand each other."

At this comment, a few people giggled. We were beginning to relax. Our teacher had achieved his first goal. Now that we were relaxed we were in the correct frame of mind to learn.

"For the next three months you will study a minimum of two-and-a-half days a week and will sit regular tests, and an interim, and then a final exam. Anyone got any questions so far?" he asked. No one had.

I listened intently and tried to visualise what my training would be like. I was looking forward to it.

Squadron Leader Evans told us a bit of his life history. "I was a fighter pilot and I decided not to retire after the war. After working in administration and stores, I joined No. 4 School of Technical Training."

I decided that I quite liked him. I liked him even more when he told us to go for a smoke break before the serious work began.

For the rest of the morning we concentrated on the history of the RAF and its structure, which included how the service was divided into commands that were then subdivided into groups, then units, wings, and then flights.

When Corporal Edison came to march us back for lunch he did not appear a happy man. His bad mood was not beneficial for us; by the time we reached G Lines, four people were destined for fatigues.

After a morning in the classroom, the whole of the afternoon was spent on the parade square, and none of the DIs appeared content with our progress. Their incessant snide remarks and punishment for doing nothing wrong was starting to piss me off, but I decided to grin and bear it and try hard to avoid fatigues. The rest of the week followed the same routine: education, drill, more drill, physical training, more physical training, more education. It was a tough programme.

******

The part that I enjoyed the most, which surprised me, was the education. We moved on to the theory of flight with Squadron Leader Evans. He explained how birds were able to fly, relating this to cover the relationship between thrust, drag, lift and weight. By the end of the week I had a good understanding of the forces required to make an aircraft fly and the characteristics of wings and aerofoils.

After three weeks' training, my feelings towards the RAF were a mixture of love and hate. The love bit was the education, and I liked the food and comradeship. I did not mind the marching and the bull or the inspections. What I did hate, with a vengeance, were the fatigues and the DIs, plus some of the catering staff, who treated me like I was less than human.

There never seemed to be any good news, so when Corporal Brand told us that we could apply for an off-camp pass everyone was delighted. The joy diminished a little when he told us that the passes would be spread over the next three weekends to avoid several hundred boy entrants invading Barry Island and upsetting the local population. The pass would start at 12:00 hrs on Saturday and would end at 21:00 the same day. I never applied for a pass. Why? What could I do with half-a-crown, or whatever remained of it after I'd bought essential Duraglit and cigarettes?

On Monday morning, we marched to the armoury and were each issued with a rifle.

"Let's hope you can do rifle drill better than you can do foot drill!" shouted Sergeant Coffee.

I don't know whether it was because the rifle helped me keep my balance, or whether it was the fact my drill movements were improving, but I did not drop the rifle once, unlike others who had to suffer the consequences. Fatigues loomed on the horizon for them that evening.

I practised all the drill movements that I'd learned previously, plus the additional movements of slope arms, present arms and order arms. Corporal Brand shouted out the timings using numbers. At times the noise of boots coming to attention was deafening, alongside the din of hands and arms slapping against rifle butts. By Friday I thought that we were starting to look like proper airmen, but not a word of praise was emitted from the mouth of the DIs.

After five weeks of training I had been to the cinema twice, played football three times and the only female that I had spoken to was Carolyn, who served in the NAAFI. I had joined a group with similar interests to me and we were all getting along fine. We had a favourite saying: 'Don't let the bastards grind you down.'

Life was not full of surprises, but it was filled with situations that had to be overcome and achieved. Good or bad, you just had to get on with it.

******

The new timetable in the seventh week showed that we would be assessed on the performance of the previous six weeks. Our DIs would assess everyone, and those who failed to meet the expected standard would have one-to-one instruction. I did not fancy that.

There would also be a mid-term exam covering the educational subjects we'd completed. Failure in any subject would result in extra training. If anyone failed more than one exam, they could be remustered to the catering corps or the RAF regiment. I didn't want to be a cook or a rock ape. I decided that I needed to do a lot of studying to maintain my current status.

On Monday morning I expected to be on the square, but that day Sergeant Coffee had other ideas. He ordered my flight to fall out and head back to our billets, to change into our denims and fall back in again. I fully expected that we would be doing fatigues, but I was wrong.

Corporal Brand marched us to the RAF regiment compound, where a sergeant rock ape was waiting with four other rock apes.

"Right, listen up," bawled Sergeant Rock Ape. I was now convinced that rock apes had a very limited vocabulary.

"Today, we are going to start ground defence training (GDT). Because of limited space in the classrooms and range, you will be trained in four separate groups. You are the first group."

My flight was split into four smaller groups and my group was designated 'Squad 2.' We were told that we should enter the complex and occupy the room that corresponded to our squad number.

Once inside, I saw posters on the walls and several exhibits of guns. Corporal Jones and an enlisted rock ape were there to teach my group firearm safety, about different types of guns, and how to strip and maintain the .303 Enfield rifle, the STEN and Bren guns. I enjoyed the first class. The rock ape instructors were quite human, and no one ended up on fatigues. I felt quite satisfied by the time I marched back for lunch.

At the next education session I had a new teacher called Flying Officer Baldwin, and the class advanced to electrical theory training. Once more, I liked my teacher. When I got into difficulty with the mathematics associated with the various electrical laws, he was patient and helpful. Remembering how to transpose the formulas was not easy, and I could tell from the posters on the walls that the formulas would only get more difficult.

******

I joined a study group to help with the revision for our assessments, but we had one major problem: fatigues. At least one person did fatigues during study times. I did six nights on fatigues in the cookhouse. I hated fatigues as much as the little snide of a cook, Ryland, hated Scotsmen.

However, when assessment week arrived I felt I had done everything I could to prepare and be successful.

The first assessment started with relentless foot drill, with the four DIs calling out the commands and Sergeant Coffee with his clipboard making notes. It was the first time I'd seen him with nothing to say.

In the afternoon, Flying Officer Baldwin had a bit of a surprise for us. We were going to revise before sitting the test on Wednesday morning. I think that was a big relief to everyone. At least we would have a few more hours of instruction.

Tuesday's assessments started with PEd, followed by rifle drill. In the morning the sergeant PTI made notes on his clipboard while the PTIs ordered us to do exercises. I did an hour's circuit training plus work on five different pieces of floor apparatus. I struggled on the parallel bars and the ropes. I was shattered when lunchtime arrived.

In the afternoon it was Sergeant Coffee once more, but first we had to go to the armoury to collect rifles. After an hour of rifle drill my feet were burning and I had cramp in my right leg. I kept thinking about our motto: 'Don't let the bastards grind you down'. I was extremely relieved when we returned our rifles to the armoury. Tired or not, I swotted hard to prepare for the education assessment. That day I'd been lucky because I'd avoided more fatigues.

The education assessment consisted of two papers. The first was a multiple choice question paper with 50 questions. The second had four written questions with 25 marks allocated to each one. The pass mark for both papers was set at 60%, with an hour-and-a-half to complete the first paper and two hours for the second.

When I was told to open the multiple choice paper, I read each question carefully before answering it. With only five minutes to go I had eight questions that I did not know how to answer. I followed the obvious ploy, 'if in doubt, put C'.

After a twenty-minute break, I was ready to start the second paper. For this we were given a ruler and a set of drawing instruments. When instructed, I opened the paper and was horrified. After glancing through the questions, I felt I was unable to answer any of them. I was stuck. I panicked and started to tremble. I took a deep breath and, gathering my wits, I examined the paper closely and finally spotted one I thought I could answer.

My confidence began to return as I looked at the question covering the theory of flight. In the first part of the question I had to list the forces acting on the aircraft shown in the diagram. The second part was to describe the action of the forces. The final part was to explain, with the aid of a diagram, what is meant by 'angle of attack' and 'stall'.

My faith in myself and my knowledge had returned one hundred percent, and I started to make up for lost time.

Relieved that the assessment was over, we all relaxed and discussed our answers as we tucked into our lunch.

Next morning, when we arrived at the sports centre dressed for PEd, Sergeant Lewis informed us that, as part of the assessment, everyone had to complete a five-mile cross-country run in a specified time. There would be three separate routes, one for each flight. If anyone failed to complete the course in the allotted time of one hour they would be given extra training. We had all run cross-country several times and I felt that it would be no problem to achieve the set time. My previous football training would help me. I finished almost fifteen minutes ahead of schedule. No one in my flight failed to meet the set time.

In the afternoon, straight after pay parade, we marched to the regiment squadron headquarters to sit the GDT exam. I felt confident as I picked up my pen. The multiple-choice question paper was straightforward and when I handed it in, I thought I'd passed.

It was the same after break when we had to strip down and reassemble the three weapons we would fire when we got to range practice. At 16:30 the assessments were complete and I could finally relax.

CHAPTER 16

Blood, Sweat and Tears

The pressure was off, so I went to the NAAFI with Dai Hughes, David Murray, John Baxter and Squeak. Jimmy Laurie and Mike Robertson joined us. We decided that we'd earned a night at the Astra cinema and agreed to meet up and go to the late show on Saturday night. I thought this might be risky, because we'd been advised to stick to the early show to avoid the opportunity of bullying by the more senior entries. I knew that some of our entry had applied for a pass to leave camp that weekend and guessed that the senior entries might have done the same, so I thought it would be safe to go. I decided to be brave and join the others for the late show.

Saturday morning kit inspection was the only obstacle in our way. If anyone ended up on fatigues they would not be able to go to the cinema. Luck was with us that morning, but would it continue?

We had barely entered the cinema building when the abuse began. We didn't even get as far as buying our tickets. A tall, well-built lad, plus two others who had two proficiency stripes, started to make fun of Squeak's voice. There were twenty people around us waiting to buy tickets, but I could not see a corporal or any sergeant boys who might step in to protect us if trouble started. I heard a voice from the crowd saying, "Come on, Andy, let them go, they're only sprogs."

Andy retorted, "I don't like sprogs," and, staring Jimmy in the face, shouted, "This sprog is going to be my bull boy if he comes to our wing."

I wanted to leave and thought that Jimmy did, too, because he turned as if to walk away. He took one step then turned back. He smashed his fist into Andy's face. I thought all hell was going to break loose; blood spattered everywhere as Andy fell to the floor. People dived out of the way as Jimmy moved in for the kill, but he stopped short of striking a second blow. He could see that Andy was unconscious, blood streaming from his broken nose.

I thought that we'd all be beaten up. We were probably saved from this fate when two boys with three proficiency chevrons came out of the cinema to see what was causing the commotion. One of them looked at the heap on the floor. He turned to us and said, "Get out of here before the snoops come."

As we left, I heard another of the boys with three chevrons advising Andy's mates to get him to sick quarters, and to say he tripped and smashed his nose on one of the cinema seats.

The six of us returned to the NAAFI, shaken but not bruised.

******

I was worried on Monday morning as I entered the education classroom. Had I passed?

We sat to attention as Flying Officer Baldwin entered and said good morning. As he ticked off the register he looked up and said, "Relax, I'll put you out of your misery." I knew that he would not shoot me, so I guessed he was referring to the exam.

"What do you want first, the result or the post mortem?"

In unison, we replied, "The result, sir." I guessed it would be given in alphabetical order, which meant I would be the third one to hear the news. I was right. The first two scored 64%, and 68%. I held my breath as Flying Officer Baldwin called, "Carruthers, 78%." I smiled contentedly. I had passed the multiple choice paper. As I listened to the rest of the results, I realised that I had made it into the top half of the class.

The procedure was repeated for the second paper, the written assessment. The first two were called: 60% and 68%. My name was next: Carruthers 68%. I nearly fell off my chair. I was through. The overall results were much lower for the written paper, but everyone had passed. The rest of the morning was spent on the post mortem of our answers and the subjects we would be covering during the second half of our ITS training.

When we marched back to our billets Sergeant Coffee was waiting for us. There was no clipboard in his hand.

"Now, listen up!" he bawled. "I am pleased to inform you that all of you have met the requirements for foot and rifle drill." A smile appeared on his face. This was the first time I had seen him smile. "This is not a reason to lower your standards, because you will need to practice for your ITS pass out parade."

"Now, listen up!" he shouted again. "The other good news is that I have been asked to inform you that everyone has met the standard for both physical education and ground defence training. And I have even more good news!" he roared. "Because you are so good, everyone is to … wait for it!" Was this too good to be true, were we going to get an afternoon off? The few seconds in which he paused felt like minutes.

I thought Sergeant Coffee was never going to tell us, then he continued. "Now, listen up." More seconds passed. "Because you are so good, you have been rewarded with …" and he hesitated once more, "a ten-mile cross-country run with full pack."

I could not believe what I was hearing, though I definitely heard the groans from my fellow boy entrants. I don't think any one of us thought this man could joke about anything. Then a broad smile crept across his face.

"Only joking," he chortled. "This afternoon you can relax."

The groans changed to cheers as he continued, "If anyone wants to go to the gym, the PTIs are organising a five-a-side football competition and a swimming competition. Corporal Brand is organising a football match. Those of you who don't want to take part can catch up on your letter-writing. If you want to take part in any of the competitions, you need to report to the venue by 13:30."

He finished by adding, "Enjoy your afternoon because, from tomorrow, it gets tougher."

******

I got an impressive 86% on the GDT exam, with which I was very pleased. For the rest of the week our instructions were clear: time would be spent between range practice and nuclear defence training. I was in the second group to visit the range. When we arrived I could see the red flag flying, which indicated that the range was in use and live ammunition was being used. Inside were 10 Enfield .303 rifles, a Bren and STEN gun, plus ammunition boxes.

There were three instructors, plus Corporal Brand. It was a sunny day and I felt relaxed when my turn came to go through the safety drill and the practice of getting into the firing position. The rifle felt heavy as I got down to the prone position to go through the movements of clearing the weapon, setting the sights, loading, aiming at the target, practising squeezing the trigger, counting the rounds fired, checking the rifle was empty, and getting back into the standing position for inspection. Initially, all this was done without ammunition.

When it came to my turn to use live ammunition, I was sweating and felt excited. As I got into the prone position, I felt comfortable when I heard the order to 'clear weapons'. I worked the bolt ten times as I'd been shown. After the instructor checked that the weapon was empty, he gave the order, "In your own time, load weapons."

It was warm, lying on the groundsheet. I felt a bead of sweat running down my cheek as I pushed two five-round clips into the magazine. I pushed the bolt home to cock the rifle and applied the safety catch. An instructor checked that I'd done it right.

As I lay there, I saw the cardboard cut-out of what looked like a German soldier in uniform, who had a rifle with a fixed bayonet, supposedly charging towards me. The next order I expected was the order to fire, but I was wrong.

"Get your arse down, Carruthers, or you'll get a bullet in it."

I pressed my body further into the ground. It seemed ages before he gave the order: "Target to your front, range 500. Ten rounds in your own time. Fire!"

I set the sight to 500 feet, which was the smallest distance it could be set to, even though the range was only 25 yards. Lining up the target, I pulled the butt of the rifle as tight as I could into my shoulder and gently squeezed the trigger as I'd been taught. I heard the deafening noise from the ten rifles as they were fired simultaneously. Worse than the noise was the recoil from my gun and the butt slamming into my shoulder. Grasping the rifle securely, I pulled the bolt back to eject the smoking shell. There was a horrible smell of cordite, which seeped into my nose and mouth, making me feel nauseated. I knew that I had to ignore the feeling. I could not stand up; I had to grin and bear it. I fired off the remaining rounds until my rifle clicked, indicating that all the rounds were spent. I operated the bolt ten times and laid the weapon down with the breach open, awaiting further instruction. My ears were ringing. I felt queasy and wondered if I would ever hear again.

When it was certain that everyone had fired all their rounds, one of the instructors lowered the second red flag, which indicated that it was safe for my squad to get up and examine our targets. We had previously been told not to adjust our aim, as it was more important to have a good group than to hit the bullseye. I had seven holes in a three-inch group, two that were nowhere near the others, and one hole missing, which showed that I had missed the target. Once we received feedback on the shooting session, we were told to wait outside and ask the next squad to enter the range.

My ears had not yet returned to normal, but it was now 10:30 and I had moved on to the next period. I was back in the classroom learning about nuclear defence. The first lesson explained why our country needed a nuclear deterrent and an anti-missile defence system. Some entrants were bored by these principles, but I found it extremely interesting to discover the differences between 'A' bombs and 'H' bombs and the reasons behind this type of defence. Learning about Roentgens and Geiger counters was fascinating.

Then we were back again on the rifle range for more shooting practice, using the Bren and STEN guns . I was starting to like GDT, even though I now had a four-inch bruise on my right shoulder.

This enjoyment continued until it came to the part where we had to simulate preparation for the aftermath of a nuclear attack. I wore a gas mask and moved through a smoke-filled tunnel. I could not see the person in front of me. I tripped and fell, bashing the gas mask against the floor in the process. The acrid smell in the tunnel was strong and I disliked the stink.

Nursing a sore shoulder and a blocked nose, I watched a film that showed people who had been subjected to the two nuclear attacks America had carried out during the war. I could not believe anyone could do that to another human being. Women and children had their skin burned from their bodies, and others had multiple life-threatening injuries, including missing limbs. I guessed that the exercises and films were meant to toughen us up. At the end I did not feel any tougher; I felt unwell, physically and mentally. There was a lot to assimilate and come to terms with, as I was now part of the machine that committed such atrocities.

I successfully met the requirements for firing the Lee Enfield .303, the LMG Bren Gun and the STEN Gun. STEN is an acronym from the names of the weapon's chief designers, Major Reginald V. Shepherd and Harold Turpin, and EN for Enfield . I also passed another phase test covering nuclear defence.

******

With just two weeks remaining, I knew I would soon see the back of ITS. In a week, I would sit the final education exam. The hours we spent in education had increased, which reduced the time spent on the drill square and the rifle range. The result of this exam would determine whether I went forward to trade training or whether I'd be relegated to join the 31st Entry when they arrived in ITS.

My first job that morning was to fill in a leave application. I'd be going back to Scotland for two weeks, plus two days' travelling time, at the end of ITS training. Before that I had to concentrate on two things: my final exam and our passing out parade.

The final education exam consisted of a paper with 100 multiple-choice questions that covered every subject we had studied from day one. There was no final GDT or PEd assessment. I had learned from my last exam, the intermediate, that it was important to read the question twice, then discard two of the answers and pick out the one that fitted the question best. Three hours later, at lunchtime on Monday morning, I felt I had done enough to pass.

Feeling drained, I hoped that I might get the afternoon off. There was no chance of that. By 13:30 I was on the parade square carrying my rifle on my shoulder, my bayonet swinging from my webbing belt and being shouted at by the DIs. I had no brain, apparently, and two left feet, and I'd forgotten everything I'd ever learned about drill movements. If I didn't buck up I would be on the square until midnight. So, no change in the DIs comments. We were ordered to march around the square again.

For what I hoped would be the last time, I marched to the education centre to get my results. I was apprehensive, but confident. When Flying Officer Baldwin called out, "Carruthers, 82%," I realised that I had done better than I expected. I had passed ITS and would soon be on my way to the wings for trade training. No longer a 'sprog'.

******

The square had been marked out for the passing out parade. My best uniform was neatly pressed, my webbing belt whitened with Blanco, and my face reflected in my boots.

As I marched to the square with three hundred other boy entrants, I never gave a thought to Sergeant Coffee and his DIs. I had suffered their abuse and their bullying for thirteen weeks. In a few hours it would be over.

As the station commander's car pulled up alongside the podium, Sergeant Coffee called us to attention. He gave the open order and right dress command so that the senior officer could inspect the assembled boy entrants. It seemed ages before he reached my flight. It was so hot. The excitement of the occasion and the weather made sweat run underneath my collar. I felt as if I might faint and struggled to overcome the sensation. If you fainted you would be left on the ground until a point came when you could be removed. No one fell to the ground. The final movement of the passing out parade was the march past.

As I approached the podium, Corporal Brand ordered, "Eyes right!" then, "Eyes front!"

Once we were past the podium, we marched off the square. After returning our rifles and bayonets to the armoury, I knew that the parade had been a success. I was so proud that day. I just wished that someone had been there to share the moment with me.

******

It was almost time for my leave, but first I had to collect my pay and travel warrant. I felt happier than I had for a long time when the orderly called my name. I marched up to the table and received £22.10 shillings and 6d. I was rich.

The recruits from Scotland and Ireland received their leave passes first, so that we could travel on the overnight train from Cardiff. I was told by Corporal Brand that I could either take my kit bag or just pack what I needed into a suitcase or bag. When I returned from leave I could collect the rest of my kit before moving to the wings. I didn't need his advice; my Scotland bag was underneath my bed, packed and ready.

I got a big shock when I collected my pass and rail warrant

from Sergeant Coffee. As I collected it he said, "Well done, Carruthers," and held his hand out. As I shook it, I thought, 'Was he really the bastard I thought he was?'

******

Thirty-plus Scots, all in good spirits, boarded the train at Gileston station. By the time we reached Cardiff we had made a plan. I would share a carriage with Jimmy Laurie, Mike Robertson, David Murray and John Baxter. We would put five shillings each into a kitty and those that looked to be over-18 would go into a pub near the station and buy crates of beer.

The bottles clinked together as we boarded the train. Froth burst from the bottle tops as we toasted our success. We laughed and joked about the DIs and officers, wondering how they would celebrate getting rid of us. Then the conversation turned to what we would do during our leave. Most of us talked about how good it would be to see our mates and be near to girls again. The pub and football were main topics, too. The money in our pockets would fulfil our plans for our two weeks' leave.

Talk soon returned to St Athan, as it was the foundation of our friendships. We discussed the next stage of our training. I was very surprised when John Baxter blurted out, "I'm not coming back," before he burst into tears.

After consoling him, we listened to why he could not stand to live under RAF rules any more. We told him that, if he did not return, he would be arrested for being 'absent without leave'. He would do time in Aldershot jail, which would be much worse than life at St Athan.

I was shocked when Jimmy also said he hated St Athan. He didn't want to go back, but it was preferable than military jail. By the time the train reached Crewe, the beer was finished and our mood was one of despair.

After a cuppa and a sandwich at Crewe, we boarded the train for Glasgow. We were quiet during this stage of the journey. Too much beer, and tired bodies and minds, made us doze or sleep away the miles towards home. When I left the train at Carlisle, I shook hands with my friends and boarded the train for Annan, unsure which of my fellow boy entrants would be on the return train in two weeks' time.

******

I was just in time to catch the 9:00a.m. bus from Annan to Dumfries for the last leg of my journey home. As the bus passed Barrasgate farm, I saw my father driving a tractor into one of the fields that bordered the main road. No more than twenty seconds later, I saw two of my three sisters at assembly in the playground of my old primary school. I waved, but they did not see me. As the bus passed the cemetery, I whispered, "Hello, Mum. Hello, Grandad. I'm back." The railway cottages looked just the same and the rhododendrons around the lake were dying off. As I alighted from the bus outside the post office, I smelled tomatoes in the fresh air. These were the scents of the countryside and my home that I'd missed so much.

Mrs Hendry was the first to see me. She came rushing out from the post office with a big smile on her face. She put her arms around me and gave me a big hug. "You look so handsome," she said. "Welcome home."

It was good to see the row of whitewashed cottages again, still gleaming from my hard work. As I walked round the side of our cottage, I saw that Lizzie's bicycle was not there. The back door was locked. I guessed that she'd gone to work or into town, shopping. I wouldn't be stranded outside. I took the key from underneath the mat and let myself in. The kitchen was quite warm, but I felt uncomfortable being there alone.

What was I going to do for the next four or five hours until someone came home? There was only one thing to do. I went to see Jessie. She squealed with delight when she answered the door. It was the welcome I needed. She fussed over me and plied me with food and drink. After a wonderful Scottish breakfast, I told her all about my time at St Athan, never once mentioning the abuse and cruelty. I listened to her as she brought me up-to-date with births, deaths and marriages, and similar village gossip.

Lizzie and my sisters were home when I returned to number 14. They had spotted my Scotland sports bag by the door and knew I was back. After my first letter, asking for permission to smoke, I had not sent another. I was not good at keeping in touch and I didn't think I'd get a reply from anyone anyway.

Lizzie greeted me with, "Do you want a cup of tea?"

My sisters were excited to see me and hugged me. After tea, we went outside to sit on the wall in front of the village hall. Word of my return spread quickly and we were soon joined by other young people from the village. They bombarded me with questions about my new life. They looked at me and my uniform in admiration. They were amazed at how much I had changed and ribbed me about needing a shave. It felt good to be among friends and to relax in their company.

At 5:30, it was time for my sisters to go home. My father was having his tea; he looked up as we noisily entered the kitchen.

He commented, "You look smart in your uniform. How long are you home for?"

At that moment, I wished I was back at St Athan. Life had continued as usual without me.

Next day, Jim Steel asked if I wanted to help out in the coal yard. I could tell by his tone and the way he smiled that he was not serious. I smiled back and said, "No, thanks, I have a job." Jim was pleased to see me. He was interested in my new life and asked me about my training and new friends.

After being home for a few days, I was bored. I could only meet with my old mates at night, but I sensed that our relationship was not the same. Billy and Will had girlfriends and wanted to be with them more than me. Hughie had joined the police. Ian was the only one left who wanted to socialise and enjoy himself. Every night when I went out I wore my uniform. There was a good reason for this decision. Most times, when I boarded the bus, the conductor would not take my fare. Also, I never paid to get into the cinema or a dance. There were some benefits to joining the RAF after all.

Despite this financial assistance, days before I was due to return, I began to run out of money. I decided to stay in and keep my sisters company. That night my father had gone to visit his family, and Lizzie was at the W.R.I. When she returned she asked me, "Why haven't you gone out tonight?"

"I'm running out of money," was my response.

To my complete surprise, the next day, she handed me ten pounds. She said that it was from the money I'd sent home. I felt so relieved that I had money to enjoy the rest of my leave. In return for her kindness, I decided to continue sending home three pounds a month. That's what I had agreed to do when I went to St Athan.

My rail warrant and instructions arrived in the first post on Friday morning. I only had three days left and, with more money in my pocket, I was going to make the best of the remaining time.

I had not enjoyed my leave as much as I'd expected. People had changed, just as I had, and I was thinking that it would be difficult for me to return home in the future. My father still resented the fact that my mother had me before she got married. I am sure he believed that I was a contributory factor to her death. The only way I could stop thinking about my sad past was to find company. I met up with older boys and went to the pubs in Annan, because no one there questioned my age.

When it was closing time, at 9:30p.m., the landlord made sure everyone's drinks were finished within the allotted five minutes before the police arrived. Anyone found still drinking could be arrested and locked up. I knew that if I was arrested I would be locked up because I was underage. I would appear before the sheriff on Monday morning, and if I was fined or reported to the RAF authorities, it could mean discharge from the Boy Entrant service. This didn't bother me, as I was at a stage in my life where I didn't care.

I did not normally go to the pub at Powfoot because people there knew my age. However, it was the last Saturday of my leave and I decided that I would risk it. I got on the 7:50p.m. bus going to Annan and dismounted at the road leading to Powfoot. None of my friends from Powfoot were old enough to go to the pub, so I was on my own. As I opened the door to the back bar, I could see it was very busy and I lost my nerve. I was just about to turn and leave when a voice said, "Well, if it isn't young Drew. You look very smart in your uniform. What do you want to drink?"

It was Don Barty. I knew that Don was a tough character, and that no one would question my age if he wanted to buy me a drink. As it turned out, I never bought a single drink all night. I paid for my beer by entertaining the customers with my stories of life in the RAF. I had a good night and was quite drunk by closing time.

On Sunday April 11th the weather was beautiful, so I went fishing to clear my hangover. I couldn't concentrate on what I was doing because I kept thinking about St Athan. I knew that I would return but wondered if others would not. Going 'AWOL' (absent without leave) was a very serious offence and Colchester jail was no place to end up. I had been told that it was run by the army, and once you went inside, your spirit was broken. After such harsh imprisonment few led a normal life once released.

******

That evening, I went to the cinema with Ian and we watched 'Doctor at Large' starring Dirk Bogarde, Muriel Pavlow and James Robertson Justice. The film did nothing to boost my spirits.

"Let's go to the Empire café to round off the night," I suggested. "We can listen to the new records on the jukebox and maybe chat up some girls." Guy Mitchell's rendition of 'Singing the Blues' did not lighten my mood. Reluctantly, I said my goodbyes and took the last bus home. Everyone was in bed, but my sisters were not asleep. They'd kept awake so that they could spend a last hour with me. I appreciated their love and concern.

My father was already at work and my sisters were preparing for school by the time I dragged myself out of bed. Lizzie was donning her coat, so I assumed she was heading for work, too. She shouted, "I'll see you later."

I made sure that my sisters didn't miss the bus for school. Now I had nothing more to do until they came home. I decided to spend some time with Jessie and say my farewells to her. She cooked me a breakfast and gave me a big hug as I left her behind. To fill the endless hours before my departure, I went fishing.

CHAPTER 17

Almost There

Leaving my sisters was hard, but I knew that I had to go back. Whatever would greet me at St Athan, good or bad, I had no choice. I realised that there was no future for me in Scotland. The dreaded hour arrived. Lizzie had put sandwiches in my box and wished me luck. My sisters came to wave me goodbye. They hugged me and shouted farewells as I slung my Scotland bag over my shoulder and boarded the ten-to-five bus. I waved from the window as they followed the bus until it went too fast for their legs to keep up. I was on my way. I wondered who I'd meet up with at Carlisle.

Once I got off the bus I counted my remaining money and managed to buy six large bottles of beer from the pub opposite the station. The barman looked at me suspiciously, but I was in uniform so he did not question my age.

When the train from Glasgow to Crewe finally arrived, Jimmy Laurie was hanging out of the window shouting my name as his carriage passed. Before the train came to a standstill, he had the door open and had stepped on to the platform, followed by David Murray and John Baxter. There was no sign of Mike Robertson. We had fifteen minutes to get some refreshments and board the train. I did not ask why Mike hadn't joined us.

After eating and downing two beers, I plucked up courage. "Where's Mike?"

Jimmy didn't hesitate. Quietly, he said, "He's not coming."

"How do you know?" I asked.

"Because his mum phoned my mum at work. She told her that Mike had done something terrible and that he'd not be coming back with us." I was shaking all over, fearing the worst. "Why, what's happened?" I asked.

Jimmy went white and I thought he was going to faint. "He stuck a lead pencil into his ear and did a lot of damage. He's in hospital and will probably be medically discharged."

No one wanted to talk about it anymore. I felt ill. He must have been desperate to avoid returning. I couldn't imagine doing such a thing to myself. Silently, we settled down to try and get some sleep.

At St Athan, we signed in at the guard room, overseen by the same big, ugly snoop who had been on duty on our first day. He already had a dozen ITS boys lined up on the road outside. It was almost half-an-hour before he finished finding fault with our uniforms and general appearance. It was not a difficult task as we'd been travelling for fourteen hours or more.

Eventually, I arrived at G Lines and was met by Sergeant Coffee and his DIs. Expecting the worst, I was pleasantly surprised when Sergeant Coffee said, "Don't get too settled in your billet. You're moving to the wings tomorrow to start the next phase of your training. Pack your gear and press your uniforms. Get this place clean before you move at 14:00."

Corporal Brand issued us with new wheel disks and the chequered hatbands that matched 'Number 2 Wing' colours. Our ITS colours were a thing of the past. Not once did I hear the standard orders, "Now, listen up!" or "Come on, chop, chop!"

I thought, 'This is too good to be true.'

At precisely 13:30 the next day, we were split into groups to suit the discipline we would study. Airframe and engines would join Number 1 Wing, and electrical and instruments would join Number 2 Wing. Sergeant Coffee and his DIs marched us to our different wings.

When we arrived at Number 2 Wing, a sergeant and two rock apes were there to meet us. Corporal Brand expressed his views pleasantly, saying "Good luck."

Baby Face Edison said nothing as they about turned and marched off back to ITS.

I was feeling quite relaxed until I heard, "Now, listen up. My name is Sergeant Sullivan and this is Corporal Ellis. Don't cross us, or you'll be in trouble."

I was allocated my billet, which was E5. Squeak was in the same billet, but Jimmy, David and John were allocated different billets. Sandy Duff and other new faces entered the room. We had left our bed packs at G Lines so there were fresh sheets, blankets, pillowcases, pillows and towels on each free bed. Immediately, I made up my bed pack and sorted out my kit and my locker. Squeak, who was next to me, and Sandy, in a bed opposite, followed my actions. Shortly after 16:30, the shrill sound of shouted drill commands filtered into the room, and a few minutes later the billet filled up with more residents.

I had not seen Andy since Jimmy broke his nose, so I had no idea what had happened to him after the cinema incident. I knew that if he was in Number 2 Wing he would make my life miserable. I was hungry and pushed this thought to the back of my mind.

Straightaway the jibes started.

"The sprogs have arrived."

"Who's going to be my bull boy?"

Within minutes of their arrival, my blankets and kit were strewn on the floor.

"Pick it up, sprog, and polish my boots," was the remark I heard. I was boiling inside but decided to play it cool.

After swaggering around, disrupting the billet, they left to go to the cookhouse. Squeak, Sandy Duff and I agreed to wait until the senior people had finished their meal before we ate. We thought it would be less dangerous, that they may leave us alone. A half-hour passed as we rearranged our bed packs and tidied away the mess they'd made.

Just as we were about to leave, the door opened and a tall individual, with three upside-down chevrons on his cuffs, came through the door. He walked straight to my bed space.

"My name's Les White,' he said. "You three are lucky, because there are only three 27th Entry lads in here."

He looked directly at me and asked, "Are you the one with the squeaky voice?"

Squeak interjected, saying, "No, I am."

"Okay," Les continued, "You are going to be my bull boy."

We had heard that when we came to the wings we would be bulling the kit of the senior entry. Any objections to this procedure would be met with an internal court martial in the billet. The result of this would be a foregone conclusion. Everyone was found guilty and the punishment was a cold bath, or worse. I could see that the first six months in the wings was going to be hell.

"Go get your dinner!" Les ordered. We muttered our thanks and left.

As we had moved quarters, it was a different cookhouse we walked towards. On the way we encountered some 30th Entry lads who had also decided it was safer to dine later than the senior entry. We did not escape the snide remarks. As we lined up, the seniors pushed past us to the front of the queue. No one commented or tried to stop them.

As I moved up the servery I recognised a familiar face. It was the cook, Ryland, who had given me such a hard time when I was in ITS.

"Hello, Scottish arsehole, where's your skirt?"

I did not reply. By the time I had my meal I must have heard dozens of derogative remarks. Outside, when I went to wash my irons in the metal trough, the water was boiling hot and stank. I felt sick, not only from the smell, but the unfriendly, tortuous atmosphere created by the seniors with whom I now had to live – or would it merely be an existence?

I did not feel any better when I got back to the billet. There were only four others present. They seemed friendly enough; they were obviously not senior entry. One of them, Lindon, told us to expect a raid that night. The sick feeling from fear and apprehension continued. I was in bed before lights out. Sleep evaded me for a while as I imagined what would happen during the night's attack.

I was terrified when the bottom door flew open and the light from the corridor flooded in. I had no time to react before I felt myself flying through the air. I crashed into Squeak's bed, which turned over on top of me. Half-a-dozen more beds were heaved upside-down. Blankets and sheets were thrown on the floor. By the time I got to my feet the onslaught was over. Except for the senior entry beds, every bed had been toppled. No one switched the lights on, fearing this would bring punishment from a higher source. Our beds were reassembled in the dark. I had no idea whose sheets went on my bed.

Next morning, when the three senior entry boys went off to breakfast, I noticed two boys making up two of the seniors' bed packs. Squeak went to Les's bed and did the same. I knew that tomorrow morning it would be Squeak, Sandy and me making up the senior entry beds.

I did not go to breakfast. I just wanted to go home. Minutes after organising my bed pack I was in my overalls swinging the bumper. The floor was in a mess from the raid and it had to be bulled. I was the junior entry, so I took the initiative. It did not help much because Roger and Phil, the other two senior entry boys, gave Sandy and me the bad news. I would be Roger's bull boy and Sandy would be Phil's.

As Roger finished giving me my instructions, the bottom door opened and a short, stocky boy, with three upside-down chevrons on his cuff and one stripe on each arm, entered the room. As he approached he looked round and seemed satisfied with the condition of the billet.

"I am Leading Boy Alan Jenkins. Duff, Carruthers and Turner, I'll speak to you later. Okay, everyone outside."

Once there I fell in with my entry. Most of the other entries had their small pack slung across their shoulder. A sergeant boy and two corporal boys were in charge of the flights.

******

Sergeant Sullivan and Corporal Ellis were present, but they did not give the orders. As we marched off, the senior entry headed for the aircraft hangars, while the 28th and 29th Entries marched towards the workshops. We followed them to the big hangars that substituted as classrooms and workshops. Corporal Boy said, "Thirtieth Entry, remain at the workshops. The rest of you, fall out."

Sergeant Sullivan then ordered us to form one flight and right dress.

A chief technician, who had been waiting for us to arrive, came over and read out our classrooms and explained their whereabouts. I felt calmer. The mindless ordering about and marching was to be replaced by the advancement of my career. My second phase of training was about to start.

The classroom layout was similar to that of the education centre, but this time the posters were of tools, cables and materials. Once the class had settled down, a corporal in a khaki dust coat introduced himself as Corporal King. He called out the register. I felt quite comfortable as he seemed a decent-enough person. He smiled and spoke to us in a normal tone of voice.

"Right, lads, let me have your attention. Hands up who has worked with tools in school." Almost everyone raised a hand.

"I thought so. We'll spend a few days learning about tools and materials. It will depend on the speed of your understanding how quickly we go into the workshops to start making things."

Everyone gave him their full attention. We didn't talk amongst ourselves or mess around. We were eager to move onto practical work. We were there to learn, which is certainly what I wanted to do.

He gave us our programme.

"The first phase of study, a two-week block, will be safety and materials. You'll enjoy the second phase as we'll be in the workshops."

He explained that we would strip and connect cables, use tools, drawing instruments, drills to make holes, and taps and dies to make threads. This practical element would last for a month. The third phase covered aircraft equipment and maintenance.

"The drill will be the same. You'll learn the theory in the classroom and then go to the workshops to do the practical."

I felt excited. This was more like it!

"Finally," he concluded, "you will go to the hangars and work on aircraft."

That made me thrilled and eager to start. He gave a brief explanation on the layout of the buildings and offices and told us that we'd have a guided tour after lunch.

Meanwhile, it was our turn to go to the workshop cinema to watch a safety film. The cinema consisted of a large, square room with a projection room at one end and tables and chairs for around fifty people. Corporal King told us that the room doubled as a large classroom and a cinema. We watched and learned what to do in the case of fire or emergency in the workshops and hangars – basically, how to use fire extinguishers and to administer first aid.

When the NAAFI vans pulled up outside, he gave us a smoke break. Those who had money bought tea and doughnuts.

After the break there was a second film, which I found a bit strange and unsettling. Its subject was security and spies. It warned us that we had to be careful of what we said when talking to strangers when we left the base. It was called 'Careless talk costs lives'. It showed people giving away secrets in everyday situations. We were reminded that we were all subject to the Official Secrets Act. I realised then that my work here was important and highly sensitive.

******

I joined Jimmy Laurie at the cookhouse. "How are you coping?" I asked.

"Not very well. I hate this place," he muttered.

I tried to encourage him, but to no avail. Andy, the senior entrant whose nose he broke, was based two billets from his. He had threatened to get him and the one with the squeaky voice. I was not mentioned. We ate the rest of our meal in silence.

Back at my billet, Leading Boy Jenkins was waiting. He relayed this simple message: "Tomorrow is a full kit inspection. You'd better make the standard."

That night, everyone would be busy with Duraglit, spit and polish and the hateful bumper. This news dampened my enthusiasm for the academic work. Corporal King gave out diagrams of tools and materials, which I had to identify. Mr McConville, my Annan teacher, had done a good job, because I only got two wrong. My mood lifted and the rest of the day passed quickly.

At dinner, the first server was Ryland, who was now permanently in 2 Wing cookhouse. Wanting to avoid any contact with him, I skipped the main course and ate two plates of soup and sponge pudding.

Laid out on my bed, I found a best dress uniform, SD hat and a pair of best boots. I did not have to guess who'd deposited them there. Not one senior entry boy was in the room. Someone mentioned that they'd gone to the early show at the Astra cinema. My preparation had doubled.

I was used to Saturday morning kit inspections, but now I had a new flight commander. It was no surprise when I found myself on a charge for having dust in my bed space. Punishment was swift. Hatless, I was marched before Flight Lieutenant Morgan an hour after inspection finished. Just when I had hoped for a quiet weekend, I was sentenced to '3 days Confined to Camp,' better known as 'Jankers'. This was the same as fatigues, but with the added torture of having to report in different forms of dress for several punishment parades and inspections each day.

After dinner, I reported to the indoor parade ground for my first Jankers parade. It was a short inspection by the orderly officer. I had the bad luck of being put on another charge. My buttons were dirty. My silent reply was, 'It should be Roger here, not me. He went to the cinema while I polished his buttons and forgot my own.'

This time, we escaped a drill session. Instead, it was back to the billet to change into fatigues and report to the cookhouse for pan-washing. I was dreading Ryland being on shift. Thankfully, he wasn't.

The next parade was at the guard room fifteen minutes after reveille. As I lined up with the others, I prayed that it would not be the big, ugly snoop, who I'd encountered twice before. I almost collapsed when I saw that my fears had been realised. I figured that there was no way he could find fault with any of us as we were clad in our fatigues. Wrong again. He did find fault. My beret was not correctly placed on my head. Luckily, I only got a warning, and five minutes later I was on my way to the cookhouse.

As I entered the servery, my day, which had not started too well, went from bad to worse. Ryland was there, waiting with his usual sarcastic smile on his face. My day took another turn from worse to terrible. Ryland had an armband with two corporal stripes on his arm. I was ready to run, but had second thoughts. I thought, 'This bastard isn't going to grind me down. I will survive.' And I did.

******

The first practical session in the workshops began when Corporal King gave us all a one-eighth-of-an-inch drill, the smallest standard drill. He remarked, "The sign of a true tradesman is someone who finishes his training with this drill intact."

At the end of the tools and materials phase, I can proudly state that my drill was still intact.

I had gone from being verbally abused by Sergeant Coffee and his DIs to being bullied by boys two years older than me. After almost four months in the wings, I had endured everything that had been thrown at me. I was enjoying the workshops and had passed all the end-of-phase tests. I experienced the teaching of two more NCO instructors: a corporal and a sergeant. Both were decent and treated me fairly. The topics were interesting, and I felt that I was making good progress.

Not everyone was content. Squeak sobbed in the night and Jimmy Laurie was still not happy. Andy, the bully, had warned him that it was only a matter of time before he got him back for the broken nose.

When I tried to reason with Jimmy he said, "Don't worry, I have a plan." He did not elaborate any further.

I was talking to Roger, who had mellowed since I became his bull boy. I was shocked when he said that my idiot friend from Scotland was going around the camp pulling a piece of rope behind him. I looked puzzled and asked, "Why's he doing that?"

"I've no idea," he replied, "but he's telling people that he's taking his camel for a walk."

Needless to say, Jimmy was soon charged and put on Jankers. After several spells on Jankers, he got seven days in the guard room jail. I pitied him having to be in the same room as the big, ugly snoop who gave us a hard time.

The night following Jimmy's release, after lights out, the senior entry came on a raid. Next day, Roger told me that once the raid was over and people had gone back to sleep, Jimmy had gone to Andy's billet and switched the lights on. Before anyone could react he had pulled Andy out of bed and screamed, "I don't mind you tipping my bed over, but leave my camel alone or I'm going to stick your head in the cookhouse water trough."

Jimmy was pinned down and on his way to the guardhouse before he could do or say anything else. A month later, just after Andy's entry had their passing out parade, word came through that Jimmy had been medically discharged. His plan had worked.

First it had been Mike, now Jimmy. Who was next, I wondered.

******

One Saturday afternoon after a football match, I was approached by a scout from Cardiff City. He said that if I could get out of the Boy Entrants, Cardiff City would sign me up on a professional basis. I thought that my dream of becoming a famous footballer might be on the horizon. I could be the next to leave the Boy Entrants. My hopes were high.

On Monday morning, I told Sergeant Sullivan what had occurred. He said "Leave it with me."

A few days later, I was marched in front of our squadron commander. In a few swift words he told me, "There's no chance of signing for Cardiff City. You've signed a twelve-year contract. The only team that you'll play for is one in the RAF."

I was in and out in less than a minute. I felt let down, but had to accept my fate.

I was dreading my sixteenth birthday. I hoped that, as it landed on Sunday, the senior entry would be out for most of the day and it would pass unnoticed. How wrong could I be?! I was lying quietly on my bed when several pairs of hands grabbed me, put a hood over my head and tied my hands. I heard my big locker being emptied before I was pushed inside. The door was slammed shut and secured with rope.

I screamed for help as the locker was pushed and shoved around by people shouting and laughing. I thought that I was going to die when I felt the locker tip over and fall to the floor. I shook and rattled inside and I think I passed out. I don't know how long it was before Sandy opened the locker door.

"Get out. They've gone."

Shaking uncontrollably, I crawled from my torture chamber. I wanted to die.

******

On Wednesday it was pouring with rain and I did not have any enthusiasm for football. I moaned to Sandy about the horrible weather and he suggested that we signed for judo that day.

"You only watch on the first visit, and it's dry inside."

Sergeant Berridge, the judo teacher, was a little, round man. He'd been permitted to extend his service to beyond the 55 years' age limit. He was one of the discipline NCOs in Number 1 Wing, so I'd had very little to do with him. My first impression of him on the day I skipped football was positive. He had a gentle attitude and the judo players respected him. At the end of the class, he waited for Sandy and me to come down from a small viewing balcony and asked if we had enjoyed watching the class. We both agreed that we had.

"There's a session tomorrow night. Why don't you join it? There's plenty of club suits for you to borrow."

"Thank you, sir. I'll be there," I responded.

Sandy merely thanked him.

The next night was the first time I had ever been on a judo mat. The class began with instruction on how to break your fall and progressed to foot movements and how to hold your opponent. By the end of the class, I had carried out my first judo throw.

Two months later, I was a novice yellow belt on my way to Pontypridd Judo Club for my first competition. I won my first bout and felt that judo was the sport for me. Football, from then onwards, took second place in my life.

******

Once the 31st Entry arrived it was the same old routine of bed tipping and bulling dished out by the 28th, who were now the new senior entry. Now it was the turn of the 31st to take the brunt of the work and the abuse that came with it. As a 30th Entry, I was proudly wearing my first proficiency stripe.

Due to the incident with Jimmy Laurie and his camel, I thought that life would be easier. Once again I was wrong. I could not believe that, at the first kit inspection after the new entry had arrived, I got three days Jankers. Sandy Duff succumbed, too. What had I done wrong this time?

As the flight commander inspected me he uttered the words, "This man needs a shave!"

I silently cursed him, as I only had 'bum fluff' on my face.

From then on I was determined not to do wrong or antagonise anyone. I did not want my punishment extended further. As Sandy and I entered the cookhouse, I saw that Ryland was absent. This was a great relief and the first night passed without incident.

The next morning, straight after reveille, Sandy and I were lined up outside the guard room. A snoop, who I did not recognise, ticked off our names and read out where we had to report. It was the dreaded cookhouse again for Sandy and me. I assumed that Ryland would be there; sure enough, there he was.

Looking around, I could see that there were only a few dirty pans and metal trays to wash. I thought that we would be out of there quickly. Unfortunately, Ryland had other ideas. He said to the other lads, "Right, you lot, you're scrubbing."

Turning to Sandy and me, he said: "You two good-for-nothings, you'll know about making porridge. This porridge is not your horrible Scottish porridge, made with only salt and water. We make our porridge with milk. Fill that pan half-full of water and when it's warm, add twelve bottles of milk."

He turned and headed for the office where the night sergeant was doing his paperwork. I could see Ryland laughing and as he closed the door, I just caught his comment to the sergeant, "Stupid bloody Scotsmen."

Sandy did as Corporal Ryland directed and half-filled the pan with water then turned on the gas. He was about to take the silver top off a milk bottle when I said, "Hang on a minute, I have an idea."

Sandy looked puzzled.

"What were his exact words?" I asked.

"Half-fill the pan with water, and when it's warm add twelve bottles of milk. Then heat it up."

"No," I explained. "His exact words were: fill that pan half-full of water and when it's warm add twelve bottles of milk."

"What's the difference?" Sandy asked.

"I'll show you."

I turned the gas up full and waited five minutes until the water had started to bubble. I then placed the twelve bottles of milk, one by one, into the water.

Almost immediately, the twelve bottles of milk played a rhythm of 'chink, chink, chink' in the bubbling water.

The other defaulters started to laugh. Ryland, hearing this, rushed out of the office just in time to see the silver tops lift from the bottles and rockets of milk shoot up and spew all over the gas range. I thought Ryland's cheeks were going to burst.

The night sergeant came out to see what was happening. The only thing he asked of Sandy and me was, "Explain."

I told him exactly what we had been told to do, using Ryland's exact words. The night sergeant stared at us, as if trying to work out whether we had done this intentionally. I noticed that the cookhouse was filling up with boys coming for their breakfast. He looked at the newcomers and back at us and seemed to have made a decision.

"Right, lads, get this mess cleaned up. Get your breakfast and be off to work. Corporal Ryland, my office please, I need to have a word."

That was the last time I spent Jankers in the cookhouse.

Word of my prank spread quickly. Sandy and I had gained a bit of respect as we had got one over on Corporal Ryland.

In the following months I worked hard. I progressed up the technical ladder of learning and gained my second proficiency stripe on my arm.

As for football, I played in goal for the St Athan team against Halton, Cosford and Locking. Our team lost against Halton and Cosford.

In judo, I was more successful. I progressed through the judo grades to green belt and once again enjoyed sports.

As Christmas leave approached, I was not sure what to

do. We were all given the choice of going home or remaining on camp. Dai Hughes opted to stay on camp. I wanted to go home to see my sisters, but I did not want to go alone; consequently, I asked Dai to visit my home to celebrate Christmas with my family. He readily agreed and informed Sergeant Sullivan so that his rail warrant could be issued to Annan.

The journey to Scotland was similar to the previous one. We bought crates of beer, told jokes loudly, and chatted about women and football. Sadly, Mike Robertson and Jimmy Laurie would never be part of my journey home again. Instead of them, there was a Welshman.

CHAPTER 18

The Final Phase

It was a surprise for all the family when Dai walked through the kitchen door with me. There was a moment's silence before he was welcomed into the family. My father had to arrange an extra bed, so that Dai could have a bed to himself. It was good fun with five of us sharing the one bedroom. We told stories and jokes and played board games the girls had got for Christmas. My sisters made sure that Dai and I always looked smart when we went out. Our leave passed far too quickly.

I enjoyed my leave more than the first time. As usual, my sisters were there to see us off and Lizzie had made enough sandwiches for both of us. When Dai shook her hand she said, "I'm glad you enjoyed your visit to Scotland.'

It would not be long now before I was part of the senior entry, but first I had to participate in a summer camp at Woodvale. This camp was meant to build character and toughen us up. We slept under canvas on safari beds and ate our meals in the open air. I learned about reading a map and using a compass, but still got lost in the sand dunes. I was not very good at map-reading.

The best part at summer camp was the flying. Everyone took their turn to be taken up in an Anson or Chipmunk aeroplane for a flight around Blackpool Tower. There was a lot of sick people that day, due to the pressure changes in the plane as it circled around the tower.

The atmosphere around the camp was more like what I had seen on American films. Although it was hard, it was fun. Like the Americans, we sang songs as we marched.

By the time I returned on the troop train to St Athan, I was looking forward to the rest of my training, because I would soon be senior entry with all the perks that went with this.

My final phase would start after the 29th Entry had their passing out parade and the 30th became Senior Entry. I would then have my three proficiency chevrons on the cuff of my sleeve and have all the senior entry privileges.

March 27th was a dull, wet day and the passing out parade for the 29th Entry took place at the indoor drill hangar. Not only was it a big day for the 29th, it was also my big day. As the 29th Entry marched off the square I knew my turn had arrived. I was now senior entry.

As some of the 29th were showing their parents around the camp and getting final signatures on blue departure cards, the 30th were preparing to hoist a white bedsheet marked with their emblem and entry number as high up the water tower wall as we could get it. This was a traditional event that would indicate to everyone that the 30th Entry now ruled the other entrants.

One of the privileges I was looking forward to was being able to wear civilian clothes. Senior Entry could wear a blazer, flannels, white shirt and tie to go off camp. Most of us could not afford blazers, so we bought second-hand ones from the outgoing 29th or we'd share. When I went to the towns in the valleys to compete at judo, I could wear civilian clothes. I still could not go to dances, because I had to be back in camp by 22:00. Since arriving at St Athan just over a year previous, I had only left camp to play football or to visit other judo clubs.

I hoped that my life as a senior entry would be easier, but I knew from previous experience that nothing was easy at St Athan. Once the initial feelings of having a bull boy and going on raids after lights out wore off, it was time for hard work to restart.

I knew that there would be extra drill sessions to prepare us for our passing out parade; this didn't bother me. My fear was the oral boards. An ex-28th Entry lad, who was now stationed at West Camp and was also a member of the judo club, had told me about the oral board and it frightened me. Fortunately, over the next few weeks he gave me some coaching.

With only a month to go, I was well prepared. I could hardly wait for the day to come when I would leave St Athan East Camp. Sergeant Sullivan gave me a form to fill in, where I had to make three choices as to where I would be posted after my training was complete. I chose St Athan 32 Maintenance Unit, located on St Athan West Camp. This was my first choice, because I wanted to continue my judo training. I was not bothered where else I could be posted to, so I wrote no preference.

******

With just three weeks to the end of our training, it was time for the final trade tests. They were to be conducted over a period of two weeks by the Trade Standards and Testing Section (TSTS), whose reputation for failing people was well known. Failure to meet the standards would mean relegation to the 31st Entry.

I had taken several practice papers and noticed that there were a number of questions that were repeated on each paper. I was hoping that they would be repeated on the final paper. After an hour of the allotted two hours to complete the final test paper had passed, I was struggling. I had not seen any questions from the practice papers. Thankfully, I managed to confidently answer more than half the 100 questions.

Next day the oral boards started. I had not slept much the night before and was literally shaking at the knees when a chief technician wearing a brown dust coat and carrying a clipboard came into the classroom, calling out six names. Mine was one of them. We were escorted to the workshops where three senior and two chief technicians were waiting to greet us.

When my name was called a chief technician said, "You're with me."

I was surprised when the examiner asked me, "Where's your home? Have you enjoyed being at St Athan?"

We chatted for a few minutes then he asked his first question. I was not expecting the sudden change; however, it was a simple question. "Can you tell me what colour the warning lights are on the port and starboard wings of an aircraft? "

"Port red, starboard green," I replied.

"Good, that's not so bad, is it?" the chief said, then he continued to ask me more questions.

When we moved to the next bay, which was filled with switchgear, I relaxed and answered his questions confidently. After two hours, I was told to return to my classroom and wait until I was called again. I felt I had done quite well but thought that it would probably get harder.

I was not called again that day; however, the next day I was one of the first six to be called. This time I was with a senior technician who also put me at ease before he grilled me on voltage regulators and aircraft starting systems. The time seemed to pass quickly, because when I returned to the classroom I noticed that the clock had moved forward two hours. I was called again in the afternoon to demonstrate the use of tools and test equipment. I felt comfortable that I'd performed to the best of my ability.

By lunchtime on Friday, I had finished the oral tests and worked with two of the examiners twice. I felt that I had correctly answered the questions on batteries, static and rotating equipment, but had been not so precise with the information about the 24-way bombing system. I had no more studying to do as the final test would be about airfield operations and safety.

When Monday morning arrived I was ready for it. There were group exercises where we marshalled aircraft, and individual exercises that covered documentation and how to enter the cockpit of an aircraft that had an ejector seat fitted. I knew that if I failed this phase then I would fail the whole exam. I concentrated hard, and by the eighth day of testing, it was all over. I was afraid to even think about how well I had done. Secretly, I was quite confident that I'd passed.

Now I had the weekend to look forward to, I gave myself no more time to consider my failures or successes. I was going to the Leicester Police Judo Club for a match on Sunday, which would occupy my mind. Nevertheless, I was mentally tired and I lost my bout. A niggling fear of failure kept emerging in my mind.

We had just over a week to go before our passing out parade. Sergeant Sullivan did not allow us to be idle. On Monday morning it was back to square-bashing and PEd. I think it was a ploy by the RAF to toughen us up before we entered the main arm of the service.

By the time Wednesday came, I thought that they were trying to kill me. My feet burned, and my muscles ached all over. Once more I was subjected verbal abuse, which made me feel that I was less than human.

Wednesday afternoon would normally have been sports day, but instead, it was results day. I reported to my workshop classroom, where I'd receive good or bad news.

From the post mortem, when we reviewed the questions, I knew that I'd done reasonably well, and this was confirmed when the results were read out. I scored exactly 80%. I was very pleased. It wasn't the highest mark, but it was in the top half of the marks given.

I held my breath when it was time to reveal the practical mark. When I heard '70' I almost collapsed, and then I heard '4'. I had done a lot better than I expected. As I listened to the rest of the results, I realised that 74% was a very good mark.

I was happy that none of my close friends failed. After all the marks were read out, we marched back to the billet. Due to the mental strain and anticipation, I was exhausted, but there was no time to rest.

It wasn't plain sailing after results day. It was hell practising for our passing out parade. The following Wednesday we were marched to the indoor drill parade ground where Sergeant Sullivan told us our postings had arrived.

I wasn't holding my breath in anticipation of returning to West Camp and I was right not to do so. When it was my turn, I heard, "Carruthers, No. 232. Operational Conversion Unit (OCU) Royal Air Force, Gaydon."

I had never heard of it.

When I met Tom at the judo club, I asked him to check it out. Two nights later he told me, "Gaydon is in Warwickshire, close to a town called Banbury. It's a training unit for 'V' Bombers. The Hadley Page Victor V Bomber is based there. You lucky so-and-so. It looks like you're going to be a part of the V Bomber Force."

Next day, when I talked to Sandy Duff, I discovered that he had been posted to St Athan West Camp. He suggested that we should ask for a swap. He did not fancy being based at West Camp whilst it had been my first choice.

Sergeant Sullivan told us that it was not possible to swap the posting, but we could apply for an exchange posting, which might be looked on favourably if we applied right away. He helped us to fill in the forms and he submitted them.

On Saturday afternoon, almost all the 30th Entry signed out at the guard room, ready for a final visit to the local city. This would be our last opportunity for a night out before leaving St Athan. I had not been to Cardiff on a night out, so when Sandy suggested an alternative to Barry Island, where most of the others were heading, I readily agreed. We remained on the train until it reached Cardiff.

I explained to the ticket collector that we had changed our plan, because this was our last weekend before being posted away. I explained that it might be our last opportunity to visit Cardiff, a place we really wanted to see. He smiled and let us go through.

We decided to start at the cinema, and when we flashed our 1250 ID cards the ticket lady let us in for free. We watched 'Dracula,' starring Peter Cushing and Christopher Lee. After what we considered an enjoyable film, Sandy suggested having a couple of beers to pass the time before going on to

Tiger Bay. That was where we were going to have a Chinese meal before heading back to base.

It was the first time I had tasted Chinese food and I thought it was delicious. When we finished our meal it was still early, so we walked aimlessly around Tiger Bay. As we passed a place called the Blue Moon Club, which displayed pictures of women wearing few items of clothing, the guy at the door asked, "Are you coming in?"

This time, Sandy did the explaining. He told him that it was our last weekend before we were posted to some God-forsaken place in the desert. He took pity on us and let us in for free.

Inside, approximately twenty men were drinking beer and making rude remarks to a woman doing a strip-tease on the small stage. By the time we got a beer, she was almost naked.

"Get it all off!" the men shouted.

"She will for a couple of quid," the barman remarked.

The men clubbed together, and within minutes, I was watching the first naked woman I had ever seen parading around in the spotlights.

We decided to spend the rest of our money on a final beer as we watched the show.

On our way back to the station we remembered that our ticket started at Barry, not Cardiff, and that we didn't have any money to pay the extra amount. We needed a plan. This materialised on the station forecourt.

We did have enough money to buy two penny tickets to get on the platform.

We kept in the background until we saw two girls approaching. We followed closely behind so that it looked as if we were with them. As they showed their tickets and walked through to the platforms we showed our platform tickets and said, "We're escorting our girlfriends onto the train," and quickly caught up with them.

We boarded our train, knowing that nobody would check our tickets until we arrived at Gileston, where we left the train to begin our walk to St Athan. We'd had a great day out.

Within hours of receiving my new posting, I was summoned, along with several others, by Sergeant Sullivan. I wondered what I'd done wrong. Sergeant Sullivan started with the usual Rock Ape phrase. "Now, listen up," he called. "You are here because you have not reached your eighteenth birthday."

I looked at him, puzzled, while he prepared to recite his next sentence.

"Queen's regulations," he began – he was good at quoting these and I had heard the words several times during my training . . . "Queen's regulations," he repeated and paused. "Queen's regulations," he reiterated, "prevent you from joining the Royal Air Force as an adult until you have reached your eighteenth birthday. For this reason, you will not be permitted to wear your Leading Aircraftsman Badge until you have reached your eighteenth birthday. You will be fitted for new uniforms, but you will still be required to wear your chequered hatband on your SD cap."

'Thanks a lot,' I thought to myself. 'All the abuse I've had to put up with, and I have to stay as a boy entrant for another fourteen months.'

Sergeant Sullivan continued, "You will not be able to sign any official documentation, for example, the Form 700, until you reach 18. Until then, you will be treated as still under training."

When I got back to my billet I laid on my bed and felt deflated. I ignored everything going on around me.

******

At the start of the final week, Sergeant Sullivan reminded us that the following night was our graduation dinner. I had been looking forward to this, but not now. At precisely 17:00 hours I was sitting down, dressed in my best uniform, near the centre of several tables that had been joined together and covered with white bedsheets.

Several of our officers and NCOs assumed the role of waiter, and they served us a scrumptious five-course meal. Afterwards, our wing commander said a few words of congratulations, telling us that we had a fantastic future to look forward to. I lit up one of the free cigarettes thinking to myself, 'At least I'm old enough to smoke.' I was in bed by 22:00, preparing mentally for the pass out parade final dress rehearsal.

The final dress rehearsal was in full uniform, including white webbing, rifle and bayonet. It went well, with our newly-promoted flight sergeant boy from one wing supported by the three sergeant boys from the two wings in charge of the parade.

After the rehearsal and lunch, Corporal Ellis came to our billet and handed out our blue arrivals/departure cards. The rest of the afternoon was spent visiting the same sections that required signatures on the arrivals card. This took me all afternoon, but I got all the signatures except for those that could not be signed until after the pass out parade had finished. I spent the evening pressing my uniform and bulling my kit before getting into bed at St Athan for the final time.

When I woke the sun had come up, and I did not care if there was dust around my bed space. All I wanted was a decent last breakfast and to get on with the final job: the passing out parade.

At 08:00 I had fallen in on the road, carrying my white rifle sling. It took the next hour to pass through the armoury and collect my rifle and bayonet. After completing the safety checks on my rifle and fixing the bayonet into the scabbard on my glistening white webbing belt, I fixed the also-glistening white strap to the rifle. I was ready to go.

Once we were all assembled and ready, our sergeant boy called us to attention, followed by stand at ease, then prepare to fix bayonets, followed by the fix bayonet command. These were not practice bayonets but the real thing. There was no thought in my mind that anyone would mess up and drop their rifle or faint on parade. We had prepared for this day and we had prepared well.

As the sergeant boy yelled for us to 'slope arms' it was time to go. Each sergeant boy took their place at the head of the column, and I could see the station band up ahead.

Once the music started, the orders to march off were passed from the sergeant boys to the corporal boys, and it was then that I realised the parade had started. We had practised so hard for this day and, so far, it was running as smooth as clockwork.

The sound of the band was loud and clear and the Boy NCOs were calling out the orders loud and clear above the sound of the band. As we entered the square, I could see the parade commander standing in front of the dais with the two standard bearers just behind.

When all the flights were on the square and facing the dais, we were ordered to left turn and face the saluting base, followed by order arms. Several more drill movements were completed, a sergeant boy acted as the parade warrant officer. He handed the parade over to the flight sergeant boy parade commander.

When the flight sergeant boy stood us at ease, I knew it was just a matter of time before the air vice marshal would appear to review the parade. We did not have long to wait before the car arrived and he got out, accompanied by our own air commodore, who was our station commander.

As the air officers approached, the flight sergeant boy yelled out, "Parade, general salute, present arms." As the flight sergeant boy about turned and saluted, the band started to play. The words were lost in the noise of almost three hundred arms slapping against the wooden bodies of rifles and double that number of boots slamming down on the parade square. The flight sergeant boy approached the air vice marshal, saluted, and informed him that the parade was ready for inspection, finishing with, "Sir."

I was almost there. No one had fainted during the long wait, but it would be another half-hour at least before the inspection was finished. As it progressed, I could hear the sergeant boy and corporal boys barking out their orders. Then my flight was brought to attention and prepared for inspection. I was relieved when the air vice marshal passed me by without stopping to inspect me or ask any questions.

Once the inspection was over and the flight sergeant boy requested permission to "Carry on," I had almost no feeling in my legs, but I knew it was almost over. The flight sergeant boy marched up to the dais where the air vice marshal was now standing and requested permission to 'march past'. Permission was granted, and the final drill movements were called out.

We had practised hard for the march past and once again it went like clockwork. As each flight approached the dais, the order was given to 'slow march' then 'eyes right'. Once I passed the dais, I realised there was only the review and the general salute to complete. This was the most difficult part of the parade, but when the flight sergeant boy ordered us to advance in review order, I had no difficulty in doing what I was supposed to do.

The band was playing, and I was able to see that there was a number of spectators in the stand behind the review platform. When we came to a halt the order was given: 'present arms' for the 'general salute.' As the band struck up again, all the parade commanders saluted the air vice marshal as we came to the present arms' position. The air vice marshal and the other officers returned the salute and the spectators stood up as a mark of respect.

The flight sergeant boy approached the review platform and saluted before asking permission to 'march off'. When permission was given, the 31st Entry was marched into position to form a Guard of Honour. It was all over.

As we marched off to return our rifles and bayonets to the armoury I felt good, and I sensed that everyone else was feeling the same.

There were two final jobs to complete: prepare our bedding for laundry; and return our white webbing to the quartermaster's store and get his signature on our departure cards.

Only one more signature to go. We had been told by Sergeant Sullivan to be at the indoor drill hangar by 14:00. It was pay day. I had amassed almost forty pounds and, when I saluted to collect my money, I was handed a travel warrant back to Annan.

The wing sergeants and corporals were all there to collect our departure cards and wish us good luck.

On my return to the billet to collect my kit bag and Scotland bag, several lads were outside, talking with their parents. As I passed, one of the fathers put his arms around his son's neck and I heard him whisper, "I'm so proud of you." Sandy, who was with me, also heard the remark and we smiled at the lad and his parents.

Once we collected our things Sandy swung his kit bag on to his shoulder and said to me, "It's time to go." No one had come to see Sandy or me 'pass out'.

The newly-graduated airmen were in good fettle. No one questioned our age when we went to buy beer for the journey home. As I said my goodbyes at Carlisle my final words were, "See you at Melksham when we do the fitters' course." I doubted that I would see my friends at Melksham, because I had at least another 18 months to go before I could apply for my fitter training and be promoted to junior technician.

CHAPTER 19

Welcome to the Real World of Work

As I signed in at RAF Gaydon's guard room I was expecting a hard time, but it didn't come. The snoop on duty, who was just as ugly as the first one I had met, was very helpful. He drew me a map showing how to get to my billet, the position of the cookhouse and the NAAFI. He told me that once I got settled. I had to report to administration to collect my arrivals card and, if I came right back, I could collect my bedding and irons from the quartermaster's store. I thanked him for his help and started walking.

My billet was in a brick building block and I was sharing a room that contained four beds, which were already made up. I was surprised to see that there were no bed packs. There was a tannoy speaker on the wall outside, so I figured that getting up in the morning would not be a problem.

Two people in my room were national servicemen, and there was one person called Harry, who had been a boy entrant. I was wondering why I was not given a room with other boy entrants as Sergeant Sullivan had intimated, but I said nothing. Harry explained the routine and I accompanied him to the cookhouse. It did not take me long to settle in; when the others came into the room they introduced themselves. Harry told me that I should accompany him in the morning and he would introduce me to our warrant officer in charge.

I could not believe what was happening. Warrant Officer Bell was so human, and when he took me to the field office to meet Flight Lieutenant Peterson he welcomed me to Gaydon. He said he was aware that I was under eighteen, and as I was the only one in the flight who was still a boy entrant, he asked if I minded sharing with others. I readily replied, 'No, sir, everyone I have met is very nice.'

When I entered the hangar, I gasped – right in the centre was a Victor bomber on jacks. Looking around, I could see the tool store, toilets, workshops and a number of offices down the sides. As I entered one of the offices, WO Bell spoke to a chief technician sitting behind the desk, "Bill, this young man is joining us. His name is Carruthers. He is still a boy entrant, so he cannot sign for his work."

He turned to me and said, "This is Chief Tech Latimer. I will leave him with you, Bert." With that he turned to me and said, "I hope you enjoy your time with us. If you have any problems, come and see me."

I could not understand why the warrant officer had called the chief technician by his first name. I knew that I would not be allowed to do the same.

Chief Technician Latimer stood up and held out his hand. I felt nervous, but shook his hand. He told me that he was in charge of the maintenance team that I was joining and said, "Let's go. I will give you the grand tour and introduce you to the others."

As we passed through the hangar, I was introduced to Sergeant Davis, Corporal Clark, and Corporal Higgins - who Chief Technician Latimer said was in charge of my team. He then asked me my first name and I told him it was Andrew, but that I preferred to be called Drew. Chief Technician Latimer turned to Corporal Higgins and said, "Ron, can I leave Andrew with you, and you can show him the ropes?"

Moving through the hangar and meeting different people, I came to realise that it was customary for an NCO of higher rank to call a lower rank by their first name, but anyone of lower rank always called someone more senior by their rank. Officers never called any enlisted person by their first name.

As we passed a large, upside down V-shaped board on wheels, Corporal Higgins said, "Do you know what a shadow board is?"

I told him that I'd used one during my last phase of training. Its purpose was to control the use of tools, so that a tool never got left in the flying controls of an aircraft. At the end of work, if any tool was missing from the shadow board, everyone working on the aircraft was kept behind until it was found.

"Very good," he replied. "Let's go to the crew room for a cuppa."

When I entered the crew room there were around twenty people having their break. As we approached the tea urn, Corporal Higgins called out, "This is Drew Carruthers who is joining us from St Athan." There were a few remarks made jokingly and several people came to shake my hand.

******

I quickly settled in to my new job, which was to carry out any modifications that came from the manufacturer or from our own bomber command. When an aircraft was new, or it changed its role, there was always lots of modifications to be done. It was interesting work. I was treated just like all the other technicians, except that Corporal Higgins had to check and sign off my work. I was not allowed to work on anything to do with flying controls, but no one else was allowed this privilege until they had proved themselves.

One day, I was a bit surprised when Warrant Officer Bell called me to his office. You only got called to the office if something was important. When I entered he just said, 'Take a seat. You have been with us three months now and I have to make out a report on your progress."

I looked at him and had a feeling there was a bit more than just my progress review in question.

"Corporal Higgins and Chief Technician Latimer have good things to say about you: good time-keeping, you're keen to learn, and your practical skills are good, so…" He hesitated, looked at me, and said, "Why do you want to leave us when you are making such good progress?"

I had no idea what he was talking about and replied, "I don't understand, sir, I don't want to leave here."

"Well, why put in for an exchange posting?" he asked.

I had forgotten all about that. It was too late to change

my mind. The RAF did not like indecisiveness. A week later, I was on the train heading for Cardiff and St Athan West Camp and Sandy Duff was on his way to Gaydon. Both of us had to pay our own train fare.

When I arrived at 32 Maintenance Unit, I was used to getting signatures on the blue arrivals card, so I settled in quickly. I was billeted in one of the new brick-built blocks that had four to a room with the tannoy in the corridor. Most of the airmen were either national service, ex-national service, or ex-boy entrants.

I was allocated to the maintenance workshop where Sandy had been working. It was a lot different to Gaydon. The workshop consisted of five rows of benches with twenty people in each row carrying out maintenance work on all sorts of aircraft equipment. I started on electromagnetic contactors. In the workshop was the stores, a washroom, toilets, and offices where the equipment inspectors, whose job it was to inspect and approve our work, were located. At one end there was a test bay with a chief technician in charge. At the top of a set of wooden stairs was a large Perspex-fronted office overlooking the work area. This was where Warrant Officer Monaghan, nicknamed Rinti, sat and overlooked everything going on in the workshop below. It reminded me of an American factory I'd seen in the cinema.

My friend, Tom, was at one of the benches two rows across from me. On either side of me was Noddy Barker and Davy Maul. I quickly became friends with them.

Tom and I went to the judo club together. Sergeant Clarrie Berridge was really pleased to see me back at his club. The judo club was situated on East Camp; I was now based on West Camp, so I met a number of boy entrants who were still under training and who I knew.

West Camp was much larger than Gaydon and it was a little stricter. I was nominated for guard duty, which meant spells of checking people in and out at the gate and patrolling the camp at night. One time, I got the fright of my life when I was on patrol with another lad. We saw an open window, so we went to investigate. I switched on my torch and stuck my head and shoulders though the window. A giant of a man leapt out of bed and grabbed me. I thought he was going to strangle me. Minutes later, I was full of apologies when he let me go and I realised that it was the living quarters for the NAAFI staff.

I really enjoyed my work and only went out with friends at the weekend. Evenings were spent training. There were three black belts who visited the club regularly and I trained with them. As a result of my hard work I was awarded my brown belt. Sergeant Berridge, who was a second dan black belt, entered me for the British Championships in the Kyu (up to brown belt) category, that were to be held at St Athan.

It was a hard-fought competition and after four bouts I found myself in the final. I was up against the Leicester Police club champion, who I had fought in the past. After a tough five-minute bout, there was no decision and the referee decided that another three minutes were required. Three extra minutes is like a lifetime in a judo bout. By the end of two minutes, we had both been warned to attack more. As my opponent mustered up his energy, he made his move and attempted an 'osoto gari'. As his right leg came over, I lowered my body and went in underneath, pulling his right arm tight with my left hand and thrusting my right forearm into his armpit. Sensing he was in trouble, my opponent tried to lean back, and as he straightened up, I went lower. I had the perfect fulcrum and he went over.

"Ippon!" the referee called, and two white flags were raised by the other two judges. I was the Kyu British Champion. Two months later, I was awarded black belt first dan; this was just a month before my 18th birthday.

My birthday fell on a Tuesday, and on the Monday before, Warrant Officer Monaghan called me to his office. When I entered he was smiling and said he'd heard that I'd done well at the judo championships.

"I have something for you," he said, and from his drawer he took six senior aircraftman arm badges. He held out his hand and said, "Happy birthday, you've earned these."

I thanked him and turned to leave.

"Just a minute, I have something else for you." He picked up a form from the table and handed it to me. "Fill that in and give it back to me by the end of the week."

I looked at the form. It said, "Application for junior technician training."

I smiled and said, "Thank you, sir. I won't let you down."

As I walked down the stairs I felt that I'd grown up, like a man in charge of his own life.

I went out that night to celebrate. The rest of my life was ahead of me, and all my boy entrant days, behind me.

CHAPTER 20

They Speak Welsh, Don't They?

It was the luck of the draw whether you spent Christmas and New Year at home with your loved ones or you spent it on camp doing guard duty. Noddy Barker and I were just unlucky. We drew the short straw and were on guard duty over the Christmas holiday. The good thing was we got two days off in lieu. Normally, I would have added them on to New Year, which would have then given me four days off. I was not going to do that.

During our rounds on patrol, Noddy talked about his parents. I got the impression that he was spoiled at home and given anything he desired. His latest Christmas gift was a Matchless 250 CC motor-cycle but he needed to take a crash course to obtain his licence before he could use it. Noddy had already booked a week's course and planned to return to St Athan with his new motorcycle. He explained to me, "If I pass my test we can go out at the weekend and see Wales."

I replied, "Great, we can try and find a place where the people speak Welsh."

Four weeks later, Noddy was true to his word; after successfully getting his licence, we planned our route. Our planning was skimpy, we really had no idea where we were going. We just assumed that once we reached the valleys the villages and towns would be teeming with Welsh speakers.

So, one Saturday morning we prepared to set out on the road. We were suitably dressed: Noddy had on his full leathers and I had borrowed a leather jacket and crash helmet. It was freezing as we set off from St Athan. We had no map to guide us; our preparations hadn't run to such details! Luckily for us, because I'd visited the valleys for judo matches, I recognised some of the place names. We ended up in Pontypridd. It was a beautiful, very cold morning, but the freezing conditions did not deter us from reaching our goal.

A woman carrying shopping bags approached and I very politely asked, "Can you help us? We're trying to find someplace where people speak the Welsh language."

The woman looked puzzled. She asked me, "What language is it that you're speaking?"

I replied, "It's Scottish. I'm from Scotland."

She looked at Noddy and me and laughed as she told us, "You have as much chance of hearing people speak Welsh in Scotland as in Pontypridd. We only speak English here."

I should have realised this, because I'd been to a judo match in Pontypridd and I'd only heard them speak English. I was determined that we would not return to St Athan after failing in our quest, so I asked Noddy, "What do you think, shall we go on or go back?"

Noddy replaced his helmet and said, "Let's go on. It's too early to go back." With that he kick-started the motorcycle and I got back on the pillion. I thanked the lady as the bike pulled out and we headed for the main road to Merthyr Tydfil.

I could hear Noddy singing, but I could not hear well enough to make out the words. I recalled how, when I'd first arrived in Wales, I'd thought it was Welsh the local people spoke, until I realised they were just like me - they simply had a strong, local accent.

Noddy stuck his thumb up, signalling if I was okay. I tapped his shoulder and stuck my gloved thumb in the air as a reply. I had no idea where we were. We had passed through several villages, all totally unknown to me. I was also unaware that there was a car behind us. The road was clear of ice, at least that's what I thought. As the bike roared underneath a bridge, I felt Noddy struggling to keep it upright. The sound of metal being crushed was deafening as the car behind us ploughed into the rear of the bike.

All I remember after that was climbing out of a hedge, presumably where I'd been thrown. I sat next to Noddy at the side of the road. He turned and looked at me and smiled. He said, "We won't find any place where there are Welsh speakers now."

I looked for the bike. All I could see was a crumpled mess thirty yards up the road.

A few cars stopped, and people got out to check that we were okay. I started to feel pain, so I pulled up the left leg of my jeans to investigate. As the denim rolled up I realised that I was also rolling up flesh that had come away from the bone. I looked down and could see right down to the bone, which was covered in light-blue tendons. Seeing the expression on my face and looking to where I was staring, one of the onlookers told me to stay calm and take it easy. He walked quickly to his car and manoeuvred it closer to where I sat. A few minutes later, I was in his car on my way to hospital, my leg lightly bound with a jumper. I did not know which hospital we were heading to. The driver kept talking to me, obviously trying to keep me conscious. He kept repeating, "Keep your helmet on. We'll be at the hospital soon."

I can't remember much of what happened next, or if I thanked the driver who took me to the hospital. My only memory is of a nurse cutting the leg off my jeans and injecting what was left of my flesh with a horrible big needle. That hurt! I remember the doctor telling me to relax as I watched him stitch the flesh together. When he'd finished sewing me back together he left me with another nurse, who applied a dressing and bandage. Numbed by the injection, I felt nothing. I thoroughly enjoyed my cup of tea and biscuits while I waited for an ambulance to arrive from St Athan to take me to the RAF hospital there.

It was mid-afternoon when the ambulance finally arrived. Nurse Owen told me that Noddy and his motor-cycle were at a local garage. The ambulance was going to pick him up and take him back to St Athan as well. I thanked the people who had taken care of me and struggled into the rear of the ambulance. Twenty minutes later I recognised Noddy sitting outside the garage. He smiled at me and I heard him get into the passenger seat at the front of the ambulance. I thought it a bit strange that I was in the back of the ambulance on my own, but I soon fell asleep.

I woke when I felt the ambulance rocking as it bumped across some roadworks. Out of the window I saw that we were passing through a built-up area. I guessed it was Cardiff or Barry. I wasn't sure which one, but one thing I did know: I needed to urinate. I looked around for a bottle but couldn't find one. I thought I could hang on until we reached the hospital. The next thirty minutes were agony. I looked out of the window and recognised Rhoose. We were fifteen minutes away. The next fifteen minutes were the longest and most painful fifteen minutes of my life. When I felt the ambulance come to a halt and the handle turning on the rear doors, I was ready. As the doors opened I jumped out, landing on my uninjured right foot and leg. I continued hopping to the entrance. I knew that there was a toilet near the door. I must have looked a comical sight as I punched the swing doors open and hopped down the corridor to my goal. Never has a urinal looked so beautiful!

When I returned to the entrance, relaxation and relief showing on my face, I saw the orderly waiting with a wheelchair. Looking bemused, he took me to the examination room. There, I saw nurse Lesley. I smiled because I liked her. She knew me from the two times I'd been in isolation – once, suffering from mumps, and the other time, from measles. Nurse Lesley returned my smile and said, "What have you been up to now, Carruthers? Something stupid, no doubt."

I looked at her sheepishly and said, "Sorry, ma'am, I fell off a motorbike and hurt my leg."

Nurse Lesley looked straight at me. I thought she was going to say, "Should have been your brain,' but she did not. She told me amicably that she had to remove the bandage to check my injury. I sat on a chair with my leg on a stool and watched intently as she undid the safety pin and started to remove the bandage from my leg. As it unrolled I felt fine, until I spotted a tiny red dot of blood seeping through the fabric. The room started to spin, and I passed out. I woke up in a hospital bed and remained there for a week. Finding native Welsh speakers was never a topic for discussion from then on.

Noddy's motor-cycle was deemed a write-off. He didn't seem too disappointed; his father bought him the latest fashionable thing to replace it: a Bubble Car.

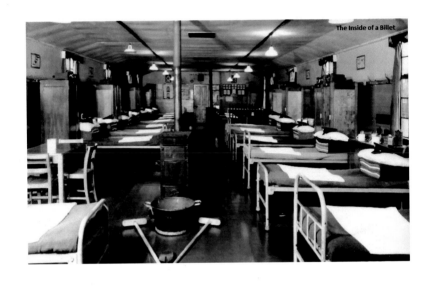

The Inside of a Billet

Passing Out Parade

The first aircraft type worked on after training

PART 3

CHAPTER 21

The Road to Manhood

Melksham is a historic market town on the River Avon in beautiful rural Wiltshire. It lies four-and-a-half miles northeast of Trowbridge and six miles south of Chippenham. My visit to the RAF base there was an important step in my life. I arrived on Wednesday 9th March 1960 to start my fitters' course, which was to last for six months. It was also where I made a very good friend, Reg Henderson.

The station layout at Melksham was similar to East Camp at St Athan; it, too, was constructed of wood. The main difference was the absence of central heating in the billets. A cast-iron coke-burning stove was the only means of keeping the twelve occupants warm. One of my room-mates was Reg, a round-faced, stocky lad who smiled a lot. Our buckets clanked together as we chatted on the way to the coke bunker to replenish our supply. I thought he was a nice guy and he must have thought the same about me, because we became instant friends.

I was the youngest occupant in the billet. The oldest was another Scotsman called Dave Jordan. Dave looked at least 35 years old. Despite the age difference, I liked him because he told jokes and stories. He surprised everyone in the billet when he went to the wash-room and returned with sucked-in cheeks and a rattling mug that slopped water on the floor. He looked as if he was entering a face-pulling competition. One of the lads asked, "Does putting your teeth in your mug make the tea taste funny?"

"Not as funny as bromide does … and be careful what you say about my teeth, or they may go sleepwalking looking for an arse to bite."

We all laughed uncontrollably.

Not much later I was surprised to see Sean Kenny kneeling at the side of his bed with an open Bible in his hands, starting to pray. We all had unused Bibles, donated by the Salvation Army, in our locker drawers. I was curious and continued to observe him as he made the sign of the cross and started to read. From his actions I guessed he was Roman Catholic. I looked around and the others were also watching him, but no one commented. After a minute or so he made the sign of the cross again, closed the Bible and put it away. Sean called out, "Good night," loud enough for everyone to hear, got into bed and pulled the sheet over his head. It was only 21:30 and the main lights were still on. The rest of us talked in whispers so that he would not be disturbed. I had never seen anyone pray at their bedside before. Sean prayed every night during the course and no one, to my knowledge, ever commented or joked about his religion.

The trainees were a mixed bunch of people; some were ex-national servicemen who had elected to sign up for an extra 18 months as regular airmen, to benefit from the extra money and training. Two people volunteered as regulars to avoid being conscripted. Poor sods, they were not aware that conscription was about to end. I was the only ex-boy entrant in the billet.

On our first Saturday morning, we had a flight commander's inspection, so no one in the billet went home that weekend. When it was over, Dave suggested going to Melksham village after dinner for a few beers. He called out, loud enough for the others to hear, "Drew, you're coming out tonight because you're the youngest, so if anything goes wrong the youngest always gets the blame!" From the tone of his voice, I knew this was meant as a joke – no bullying intended.

There was a round of applause and one of the lads commented, "Is he old enough to drink scrumpy?"

Scrumpy is a very strong, cheap cider, which is brewed in the area around Melksham. I thought that everyone was being nice and keeping an eye on me so that I'd come to no harm.

I was not allowed to take part in any of the drinking competitions because Dave thought I was too young. Consequently, the following morning, I was the only one fit enough to go for the bacon rolls.

Most weekends we were free, from finishing work on Friday, until 07:00 on Monday morning. Exceptions included: parades or inspections, if you were unfortunate enough to be rostered for guard duty, or if you were stupid enough to get Jankers.

******

By Wednesday of the following week I learnt that there would be no classes or inspections on Saturday and that most people were going home for the weekend. It was easy to travel to, from, and around the area as there was a good train service from Melksham. In addition, three people in the billet had a motor-cycle and two people had cars. Those with transport who could help offered to drop people off on their way home, if the cost of the petrol was shared.

When Reg asked me, "What are your plans for the weekend?" I told him that I would be staying on camp. He added that he would be doing the same. Reg was from Chatham and could easily have travelled home. I did not ask him why he wasn't going home; perhaps he didn't get on with his parents. I knew that I would be bored spending a full weekend on camp. It was not that there was nothing to do on camp at weekends. There was the cinema, and most weekends there was a dance in the NAAFI, plus clubs you could join and, of course, sports. But I wanted to get out and go to places and explore the surroundings - to visit places that were not associated with the RAF.

"What do you suggest we do?" he said. I proposed that we went to Bath or Bristol, but Reg was against that, because we'd have to go by bus or train and spend a night in a hotel. It would be expensive and our pay was low.

Dave overheard us talking and suggested that we

hitchhike there and back and, if necessary, find a cheap room for the night. Another lad interrupted and said, "I know the area well and it's easy to hitch a ride to Bath or Bristol. The locals are used to military personnel hitchhiking and you'll have no trouble getting a lift. Bath is only 15 miles from camp and Bristol is less than 40 miles."

I thanked him for the information and said, "Sounds like a good idea. We'll do that."

Unlike St Athan, where you could only wear blazer and flannels, there were no restrictions on what clothes you could wear off duty at Melksham. The only stipulation was that you had to look smart when you signed out at the guard room.

Reg and I agreed that it would be better to leave after lunch, as we'd have one less meal to finance. We then planned to take the first lift that stopped and go to whichever town the driver was heading to. At 13:00 we stood at the side of the main Bath to Bristol road dressed stylishly in suits, white shirts, ties and black shoes. We saw no reason to carry an overnight bag. It was quite cold, but neither of us owned an overcoat. I rubbed my hands and stamped my feet to keep warm. The first two cars to pass us were full, so no chance of a lift in either of them. The third car was a blue-and-white Vauxhall Cresta, with large tail fins and chrome bumpers. It pulled in just ahead of us. I thought it looked like a wedding car minus the ribbons, but it had stopped and that was the most important fact. The driver rolled down his side window and called out, "Where do you want to get to?"

"Where are you going?" Reg asked.

"Bristol," the driver replied.

My quick reply was, "Then that's where we're going." Reg and I grinned at one another. We were on our way to fun and excitement.

"Jump in then."

The car had bench seats and was big enough to hold six people. As the driver moved the column gear stick to put it into gear he said, "You two are very smart for a Saturday afternoon, what have you got planned?"

"We're going dancing," I replied. "We've just arrived at Melksham and we've never been to Bristol."

The driver said his name was Vic and he was employed as a company representative. The three of us chatted all the way to Bristol, mostly about the RAF and Vic's job. He mentioned that the most popular dancehall was the Glen Ballroom and, if we wanted to meet girls, that was the place to go. We reached Bristol late in the afternoon.

Vic was very helpful and dropped us outside a cheap boarding house, adding that it was easy to get to the Glen. We thanked him and waved him off before checking in.

The couple that owned the boarding house were also friendly. We booked a twin room and the lady gave us a key so that we could get in if we returned late. When she enquired about our luggage, I told her that we'd planned to go home after visiting the city but had decided at the last minute to stay the night. She took pity on us and provided us with a towel and a bar of soap. Half an hour later, after we'd polished off the plate of sandwiches she provided, we went out to see the city.

We strolled around the city centre for two hours and discovered that, despite having shared a large plate of sandwiches, we were both still hungry. We found a café and ordered sausage, egg, chips and beans. As we ate, a group of young people came in and ordered soft drinks. While they waited for their drinks they selected records from the juke-box. We spent the next two hours listening to the latest records and talking to them about everything under the sun, except for the three 'Rs'. Dave told us this meant 'religion, politics and women'.

At the Glen Ballroom lots of people were lining up to get in and, after a twenty-minute wait, we were inside the dancehall having paid the 1/9d entrance fee. The dancehall was huge and could easily hold a thousand people. The dimmed lights and rotating sequinned glitter globes made the room's floor and ceiling look like a galaxy of twinkling stars.

We watched people dancing and accustomed ourselves to our surroundings before Reg suggested that we get a beer. As we approached the lounge, a smartly-dressed man wearing a bow-tie said, "If you want food or drink you need to join the Tudor Club. That'll cost you 2/6d. You also need two photographs, which you can get from the photo booth over there. That'll cost you a shilling for four photos." He went on to explain: "You also need your birth certificate or an official document to prove you are over 18 years old."

At this point we flashed our RAF 1250 identification cards and he immediately said, "Okay, as you are in the military there's no membership charge; however, you still need to pay for the photographs."

Fifteen minutes later, I was a member of the Tudor Club; I was told to return within a month to collect my membership card. I had no problem agreeing to that. Being in the RAF was proving to be beneficial … sometimes. For the duration of the evening we danced and listened to the music. It had been a successful, enjoyable day and we fell into our beds at the boarding house around 01:30.

******

After a hearty cooked breakfast, and once we'd settled the £3 bill for the room, we walked to the A4 to wait for a lift back to Melksham. To my amazement the first car to pull up was a Rolls Royce. The gentleman passenger seated in the back seat rolled his window down and said, "I am only going as far as Keynsham, but you're welcome to get in."

I had never ridden in a Rolls Royce, and I think I would have got in no matter where it was going. The car was a shiny, dark-grey-and-silver colour with maroon leather seats that I sank into comfortably. Driving the car was a chauffeur who was attired in an immaculate grey suit, crisp white shirt and cap. I stared at the large steering wheel and the instruments set into the polished walnut panel. This car was my idea of class and splendour. What a vehicle!

The gentleman sitting next to us wore a gold chain very

similar to the one worn by a Provost in Scotland. He asked us what we had been doing in Bristol and where we were going. I told him about hitchhiking from Melksham and going dancing at the Glen. He listened with interest as I described my service as a boy entrant and how important my current fitters' course was to me.

When Reg started to talk about Chatham, I had time to look more closely at our benefactor and thought about where I'd heard the name Keynsham. Suddenly, it flashed into my mind. I recalled that I had heard it mentioned on Radio Luxembourg. It was an advert about Horace Batchelor and the football pools.

Just then the car started to slow down and I saw crowds of people gathered in the street, holding and waving flags. When the car stopped the chauffeur got out to open the door on the offside, the side where Reg and I were seated. I was the first person to step out. As the door opened, a brass band struck up and played a tune to welcome their honoured guest – obviously, not me. I did not know what to do, but my reflex action, conditioned by my time in the RAF, made me stand to attention and salute. Reg copied me. We turned to thank the gentleman for the lift and he smiled, obviously enjoying our response to the band's welcome. He held out his hand and shook mine firmly. I came to attention, saluted, about turned and walked away from him. Once they'd overcome their confusion and surprise, the crowd had a good laugh as they saw me walk away and begin to thumb for lifts again. 'A good tale to tell the lads in our billet,' I thought.

With a few more lifts we were back on camp by early afternoon. We went to the NAAFI to relax and watch the television and to discuss the weekend's events. During the week it was difficult to get a seat in the TV room, because everyone liked to catch the cartoons that were on after dinner. Yogi Bear was everyone's favourite and usually it was standing room only when he was on.

We were both in a good mood as we went to the counter to order tea and doughnuts. As we settled down, Reg started talking about himself. He'd had a brutal life at home and to escape further torment he'd he joined the RAF. When he asked about my life, I told him that I was unloved and that I suspected I was illegitimate.

"Don't you know?" Reg asked.

I told him that I did not know for sure, but I strongly suspected I was a bastard. I still did not want to believe the story that Jessie and Jock had told me.

"Okay," Reg said, "there's only one way to get the truth. Write a letter and ask. You have a right to know and if you don't ask, you will never know." He stared at me, nodding his head.

"I'll think about it," I said. I wanted to know ... but I feared seeing the words written down in black and white.

The following weeks we worked hard and played hard. The classes were getting tougher, but I still managed to pass all the phase tests and get to the Glen to pick up my membership card for the Tudor Club. My life felt happier and more successful.

The weather was improving now Spring had arrived. I discovered that it was easy to walk into Trowbridge or Chippenham where there were a few decent pubs. The countryside views and the aroma of flowers on the way made it an easy relaxing walk. There was also a taxi company based in Melksham that had pink Ford Zephyr Mark II cars in their fleet. If I went out in a group, we would arrange for one of them to pick us up after closing time.

I don't remember the particular stretch of road, but one time, four of us were on our way back from Trowbridge when we persuaded the driver to push down on the accelerator to reach 100 miles an hour. On reflection, it was a stupid thing to do, but not many cars were capable of doing that speed. It was thrilling and exhilarating to feel that speed as we zoomed past the hedgerows.

******

At the end of the eighth week Reg and I passed the phase

test. To celebrate our success we decided to go dancing at the Regency Ballroom in Bath. Luck was on our side as we only waited a few minutes for a lift, which dropped us right in the city centre. It was a warm evening, so I removed my tie, put it in my jacket pocket and nonchalantly slung my jacket over my shoulder. Reg did the same and we looked just like any other young men out for a stroll. Before we left our lift, the driver's wife told us to visit the Roman Baths. "They're an amazing historical site and still in use today," she explained. We thanked her and headed straight for the river. Roman Baths and historical education were not on our agenda; girls were.

We were fast movers; within a few minutes we were chatting up two girls, whose names were Rose and Mary. I was attracted to Rose, despite her having a brace around her teeth. Two hours later we were still with them, sitting on the bank of the River Avon drinking coke and eating crisps. I thought Rose was the most beautiful girl I'd ever met. I was in love.

I had exhausted every conversational subject I thought would interest a girl, and I wanted to stay with her longer. I offered her another coke and more crisps. Rose replied, "No, thanks, we have to go home now."

I was disappointed and asked her if we could meet them later to take them dancing.

"We can't," said Mary. "We're not 18, so we can't go." Wanting to see Rose again, I asked her if we could meet up sometime soon.

She replied, "I am going on holiday to Scotland with my parents for two weeks. We leave next Saturday." This meant that I would not see her for another four weeks. I was heartbroken.

I thought that if the girls we met were as beautiful as the city of Bath we would be in for a good time. After two hours of sightseeing, we agreed that we needed a drink. We stood outside the York Hotel, an old-style establishment with a sign that read, 'Bar open to non-residents'. It was the sort of place I liked. When we entered, I gazed around and saw high stools at the bar, so that customers could rest their elbows as they sipped their pints. Bottles were stacked in glass cupboards below the optics and the pint and small glasses were almost out of sight on shelves below the bar. We walked through a door to the 'rook', which looked more like a lounge with its low, round tables and comfortable chairs. It was quite busy with predominantly male customers. They looked quite friendly so I ordered two pints.

I nearly dropped my pint in surprise, just as I was about to take a sip, after hearing a raucous squawk. I looked up at the high ceiling, which was covered in hanging vines, and spotted a cage. The squawking came from a multi-coloured parrot whose cage was hidden in the ivy. Scanning the ceiling, I could see two more cages containing similar parrots, which began squawking in unison. As we sipped our drinks and listened to the parrots chattering away, we talked about Rose and Mary and what we thought of Bath. Time quickly passed; where we were going to sleep after our night of revelry never entered our heads.

The Regency Ballroom was smaller than the Glen, but it still had a lounge and restaurant upstairs. Tickets to enter were 2/- each. It was relatively early and the dancehall was only half full, mainly with girls. I noticed that they wore coloured flared skirts with matching blouses, long tight-fitting dresses, or tight skirts and blouses. The men wore suits or blazers, and flannels with matching shoes. Everybody looked their best for what was the purpose of the night: attracting the opposite sex.

The band played a quickstep, followed by a waltz then a foxtrot. The night finished off with a rock-and-roll session and finally the last dance was a smooch. It was a great night and I enjoyed the company of the partners I'd chosen, but all the time I was with them my thoughts were on Rose.

It was too late to get a room for the night, so we hitchhiked back. Fortunately, the roads were busy and lifts came easily; I was in my bed by 02:30. It had been a good night.

******

Over the next two weeks, I studied hard and did not leave the camp. The pressure of the hard work was taking its toll, so I felt relieved when Dave announced there was going to be a special night out on Saturday. He and some of his friends had met a group of girls from a college near Bath, and they'd arranged to spend a night in the woods drinking and singing around a log fire.

"There are twelve girls so we need twelve men to even up the numbers," he said. "There are enough cars and motor-cycles to get everyone to the wood. The cost will be £5 each to cover the food and drink. Who wants to come? Drew, Reg, how about you two young stallions? Do you want to invest in what will be a good night?"

"Yes, please!" I exclaimed just ahead of Reg's reply.

Dave was a good organiser. He arranged for a butcher in Melksham to prepare BBQ food and filled rolls, which he and another friend picked up just before the shop closed. They then collected canned and bottled beer, plus a box of red and a box of white wine, from the Bunch of Grapes pub.

On their return to the billet I played bridge until it was time to go. We drove in convoy to a pub not too close to the college. Two of the girls were inside, and they showed Dave and Paul the route to the wood. The guys returned half-an-hour later – they'd dropped the girls off so they could get back in to their college before the doors were locked for the night.

It was getting dark and we were ready to go. Reg and I rode as passengers on the back of motor-cycles while the car drivers headed to the back gate of the college, to wait for the girls to sneak out. Soon, twelve girls and twelve guys were partnered up and sat around a wood fire, enjoying the BBQ, eating rolls, drinking beer and wine. It was a lovely warm evening in June.

I had never been to a BBQ before and I was enjoying the experience. Rose never entered my thoughts. I was partnered with a very attractive girl called Carla. Carla and Rory had

217

guitars; they sang and tried to get everyone to join in. Reg was with a tall, fair-haired girl, and he looked very pleased with himself. Carla and Rory had beautiful voices and they got us into the party mood.

Reg and his stunning friend seemed to get on well. They were laughing and singing along with the others. He had his arm around her shoulders and was whispering in her ear. It was nice to see Reg enjoying himself, because he was usually quite a reserved character.

Around 03:00 it started to become quiet. Carla and Rory had stopped singing, though Rory continued to play the guitar. As Carla poured herself a glass of wine she spoke to me. "Are you having a good time?" I told her that I was and remarked that she was a terrific singer. Glancing round the fire and into the shadows she enquired, "Where's Beth and your mate? I can't see them."

"I don't know. I think they must have gone for a walk!"

"I feel like a walk. Shall we go and find them?"

"Good idea," I replied. We stood up and started our search, following the most obvious route.

Carla had sounded slightly worried when she couldn't see her friend. She expressed her concern further, saying, "We need to find them. It's nearly time to go - we have to be back in college before daybreak. We could be in serious trouble if someone spots that our beds are empty."

Suddenly, Carla whispered, "What's that noise?"

I moved forward slowly with Carla closely behind. The noise was a sort of moaning sound, and it was coming from some tall grass next to a tree about twenty yards in front of us. As we got closer the sounds became louder, and I could see what appeared to be a flashlight being switched on and off like someone was sending Morse code.

"I'm frightened!" whispered Carla. "I think we should get the others."

Taking hold of Carla's hand, I moved further forward. We were ten yards away and close enough for me to see the outline of a pair of trousers neatly folded and hanging over a branch on the tree.

I could see Reg's white bum, like a full moon in the darkness, moving up and down in rhythm to the groans.

Carla let go of my hand, turned round and beat a hasty retreat back to the campfire. I was right behind her.

Ten minutes later, Beth and Reg appeared from the moonlit path. As they approached, I could see that Beth's dress was covered in grass stains, but there was not a crease out of place on Reg's smart trousers.

They'd returned in time to help pack up and clear away the litter after our night of passion (for some) and revelry. With half-an-hour to spare before the sun rose, we took the girls to the back to the college gates. We had all had a good time, especially Reg.

******

I did not understand the significance of the Cold War; in fact, I didn't really know what was meant by the term 'cold war'. I was constantly reminded that our government considered Russia and China to be a threat to our way of life, and that a third world war could start at any time. Due to this threat, technology of war was advancing so fast it was difficult to keep up with the changes. America and Russia were building new, more destructive nuclear bombs and missiles. The world was a dangerous place in which to be born.

To cope with this threat, new aircraft were being designed to fly faster and manoeuvre better, but it was taking too long to build them. It was quicker to incorporate the new technology into older aircraft. A month into my course at Melksham, I realised that I had to learn all about the new advances. The RAF believed that a technician had to be able to carry out maintenance and repairs on aircraft systems - but it was just as vital that, should a fault develop on an aircraft's equipment or system, it was found quickly and corrected. The emphasis had switched from routine maintenance to fault-finding, which meant that I had to become an expert at using instruments, reading drawings and understanding exactly how the new technology worked.

The method of training was similar to what I had experienced at St Athan, only this time it included advanced mathematics and electronic technology. Calculus was included and this helped me to understand the principle of low-altitude bombing systems. More of my time was spent learning about navigation systems, missile guidance systems and gyroscopes. I had difficulty understanding gyroscopes.

It was hard work trying to understand and assimilate all this new technology. I realised that, unless I studied more, I was not going to get my junior technician stripe. I needed to settle down and modify my social life.

Others in my group also began to find the studies hard-going. Dave, who we generally turned to in times of crisis, suggested that we should form a study group. I'd been in a study group at St Athan and I knew that the method was successful. I could not return to my unit as a failure. I could not let myself and my unit down, so I supported the idea of the study group whole-heartedly.

The first five days of June were sunny and warm, with the temperature on the 4th rising above 28 degrees centigrade. There was no inspection or parade that weekend and I was halfway through my course. I passed the mid-term phase test, scoring 76%, and I was in the mood to celebrate.

By mid-afternoon that Saturday, Reg and I were walking along the side of the River Avon carrying our jackets over our shoulders, with our ties safely stowed in a pocket. We knew that despite the hot weather we would not get into the Regency without wearing a jacket and tie. It was such a beautiful afternoon, and the riverbank area was crowded with families eating picnics and couples holding hands as they strolled along the river bank.

It was hot and Reg asked, "Do you want to go for a coke?" Hot and parched, I agreed, and we soon discovered a suitable café. As we got closer my heart started to race: there, in front of me, were Rose and Mary, at a table with two boys, drinking cokes.

It was too late to turn back. Rose had seen us and waved us over to join them. When we got to the table she smiled and said, "Hi." She looked even more beautiful without her brace. In my confusion I mumbled, "Hi, how are you?"

She replied, "Very well, thank you."

Reg pulled two chairs over from an empty table and started talking to the group, while I went to the counter and bought two cokes. I felt jealous when Rose introduced us to Cyril and Lex. It was obvious that Lex was now Rose's boyfriend and I did not want to speak to him, I just wanted to get away from there.

When we said our goodbyes, to drown my sorrows, I wanted to go for a beer, but Reg would not hear of it. "Too early," he said. "Let's walk along the river and through the park to the city centre. We can have something to eat and then go drinking." I reluctantly agreed. We had almost four hours to wait before the Regency opened its doors.

We'd walked around Bath for over two hours and I was feeling hot, tired, fed up and sad. We decided to go a café to eat. Reg ordered ham, egg, peas and chips and, like a robot, I ordered the same. By the time Reg had finished his meal, I'd still hardly touched mine. Reg looked at me, read my mood and said, "I don't think we'll be hitchhiking tonight." He knew that I was going to drink to forget. He got up from his chair and went over to speak to the waitress at the counter. A couple of minutes later, we were on our way to a cheap boarding house close to the café.

******

"Come on, get up. It's time to go," I heard Reg say. I wasn't really asleep; I was deep in thought. When I finally emerged, I could see that he had washed his face and was ready to go celebrating. I got to my feet and said, "I won't be long." I went along the corridor to the bathroom and washed my face. It made me feel a little better. Back in the bedroom, I donned my jacket and the obligatory tie.

Once outside, we headed straight to the York Hotel and

the bar with the parrots. I sat on the corner stool at the end of the bar and Reg sat on the one next to me. The barman was a short, skinny guy with a bushy hairstyle, around 40 years old. I ordered two pints of Watney's Red Barrel and the barman replied in a strong Glasgow accent, "We only have pale ale, unless you want to wait until I go to the cellar and change the barrel."

I looked at Reg; he nodded and said, "Pale ale will be fine."

Once we had our drinks, I asked the barman where he was from. He answered, "Glasgow, but I've lived in Bath ever since I left the army ten years ago."

Reg in his wisdom said, "So, Jock, why did you stay in Bath and not return to Glasgow?"

The barman didn't smile when he looked at Reg. He said, "My name's not Jock, it's Tony, and I was born in Glasgow's Gorbals. That's why I stayed in Bath, and besides, I married a girl from Bath."

I was still thinking about the encounter with Rose when a customer ordered a 'wee heavy'. Tony took a small bottle from a cabinet, flipped the top off and poured the contents into a small beer glass.

"What's a wee heavy?" I asked.

Tony looked at me and smiled as he said, "It's a very strong Scottish ale and you really shouldn't drink it unless you want an early night."

I was not in the frame of mind to take advice and so made my order. "I'll try one."

Reg said, "Not me, I want to stay sober tonight. I want to go dancing and meet girls."

Tony looked at me. "It's up to you, but don't say I didn't warn you." He poured the contents into a small glass.

After four more, I was talking to the parrots and not making much sense. However, I remembered Tony saying, "No more wee heavies for you."

Reg took my arm. "No more drink for you tonight. If I get a girl, I'll see you back at the boarding house."

"Okay," I slurred, "let's go get a girl."

"In your dreams," Tony interjected. "You'll be asleep before the end of the first dance."

I managed to stand up straight as Reg bought the entrance tickets. Once inside, I went straight to the lounge and bought coffee, lots of it. Reg sat down and waited until I was partly recovered. "Serves you right," he told me. "You were warned."

By 11:30 p.m. I was feeling more lucid and sober. I decided that what I needed was a girl. Reg had asked a girl sitting near to us if she would like to dance. I followed them to the dance hall; everything was a bit blurred, but I could see a beautiful-looking girl with long black hair. She wore a tight dress and sported large boobs. Well, that's what I think she looked like. She was on her own, so I straightened up, went over and asked her to dance. As we smooched together, I thought she was getting a bit amorous. As I felt like getting some fresh air, I asked her to go for a walk and she agreed.

We walked for ten minutes and I started to feel better. It was getting dark and the street lights had just switched on. The moon shone down on us and I felt warm and romantic. I took hold of her hand, but I was thinking about activities other than just holding hands.

The area we were in had narrow streets and terraced houses. I could see an alley with a six-foot wall running down each side, dividing two rows of terraced houses. It looked dark enough for my plans, because it had only one dimly-lit street light at the far end and a few trees along the sides. I thought, 'This is a perfect spot; somewhere private where we won't be seen.'

We walked, or helped each other more like it, up the alley until we came to a doorway in the wall that was partly shielded by a tree. It was quite dark and cosy; I was sure no one could see us from the road. It was almost midnight and the only sounds to be heard were those of revellers in the distance leaving the Regency. I thought, 'Reg will worry about me, but if he's with a girl then maybe he won't. He'll probably think I've returned to the boarding house.'

"What's your name?" the girl asked.

"Donald," I replied, "just like in Donald Duck. What's yours?"

"Connie," she replied, giggling," just like Connie in Connie Francis."

I laughed as she put her arms around my neck and kissed me.

I thought we were both ready to go to the next stage. I took my jacket off and hung it on a branch on the tree. Connie hugged me and whispered, "You mean business."

I replied, "I hope so," and continued by unbuckling the belt on my trousers and slipping them down over my shoes. I held the trousers by the bottoms and folded them neatly, before hanging them over the same branch as my jacket. I was not thinking about Reg and I cannot think why I copied his actions from the college girls' night; perhaps it stemmed from my RAF Boy Entry training.

"Help me," Connie muttered, "unzip my dress, it won't pull up over my hips. I have to take it off." We must have looked a right pair of idiots dancing around, removing our clothes. And her handbag had somehow got caught between her legs and the dress. "Hold my handbag, I can't pull my dress down," she whispered.

I was getting excited as I took hold of her handbag and tried to hang it on a branch of the tree. It fell off and I caught it. I looked around for a safe place and tried to place it on top of the wall. "Don't put it up there," she said loudly, just as the bag disappeared over the other side and into a garden.

"Now look what you've done!" she exclaimed angrily.

"Don't worry," I said. I tried to open the gate into the garden, but it was locked.

"I want my handbag," she said, just as loudly. "Hurry up! It's getting late and I have to get home."

It was time for me to be a superhero. I jumped up and grabbed a branch on the tree. I then swung my legs to the top of the wall and lowered myself into the garden. "I have it,"

I called.

"Good. Now throw it over the wall."

Without thinking, I did as I was told.

"Thanks," she said. "Can you get out?"

I answered, "The gate's padlocked." I waited but there was no reply

"Are you there?" I called. I called out again, louder, "Connie, are you there?" There was silence.

My situation was impossible. I could not climb back over the wall and there were high wooden fences running down both sides of the garden and no gap out to the road on the other side. I was just about to scale over the fence to try the gate next door when a light came on. I thought I'd been seen, so I retreated and hid behind some tall plants at the bottom of the garden. After a few minutes, I heard a toilet flush and the light went out. To make sure everyone was asleep, I decided to wait a while. I pulled my shirt down over my legs and relaxed.

I woke when I felt something digging into my back. As I opened my eyes, I could see that it was almost daylight and an old man was standing over me, holding a walking stick above his head.

"Don't hit me!" I exclaimed. "I don't mean you any harm. It was a dare and I fell over your wall then couldn't get out. They left me here."

"Serves you right. Where are your clothes?"

I felt frightened, nervous and embarrassed. "On the other side of the wall."

"How did you manage to fall over a six-foot wall?" the old man asked. "I'm going to call the police."

"No, please don't do that!" I begged. "My friends will laugh at me."

The old man appeared a bit more relaxed. He said, "Serves you right, you young idiot. Wait here while I go for the key."

When he opened the gate, I thanked him. He laughed when he saw my trousers and jacket folded neatly over the branch. I think he'd worked out what really happened. He jokingly said, "Don't be so stupid in future, and don't lose your pants again. You could have embarrassed my wife if she'd found you."

I dressed and waved him goodbye. No doubt he was going back inside to tell his wife about the elf with no trousers sleeping at the bottom of the garden. I was sure that all his neighbours and friends had a good laugh when he told them the tale.

Fortunately, the front door of the boarding house was open and I sneaked up the stairs. Reg had left the bedroom door unlocked so I could get in. He woke up when I stumbled into the room. "What happened to you?" he asked. "I looked everywhere for you."

"You didn't look in the garden," I said.

Reg said, "What garden? What do you mean?"

"Never mind," I replied, "it's a long story and I need coffee."

******

When I arrived back in my billet after morning class, there was a letter on my bed. It was the first letter I had received since I arrived at Melksham. The post mark was Annan and the handwriting was my father's. I had taken Reg's advice and written a letter asking him if he was my real father. I knew in my heart what the letter inside would say.

I was not sure what I was feeling as I slid my knife into the envelope flap and slit it open. Inside was a single sheet of paper. I was feeling a bit queasy and not sure if I wanted to, or should have, read it. I thought about what Reg had said: "If you don't ask, you will never know."

When I unfolded the sheet of paper it started, 'Dear Drew' and that is all I can remember; except, it did say that the man I thought was my father was not. As I looked at the words, I felt an overwhelming relief come over me. I tore the letter up and dumped it in the waste basket. There was no fire in the stove so it could not be burned. Reg asked me if I was alright.

"Never felt better," I replied.

From the moment I read that letter, being illegitimate never bothered me. I have never asked who my real father was and I don't care. I don't feel different anymore. I had successfully made, and was still making, my way in life.

I was really worried when the group who had been at Melksham three months longer than my group sat their final tests. All twelve failed and returned to their units empty-handed. This was not an unusual outcome because Melksham was reputed to have a high failure rate. Their standards were very high. I knew that I would not be in the Glen or the Regency again. I did not want to suffer the same fate as those poor souls.

The final exam was only weeks away, so Dave suggested our study group stayed on camp during the weekends for extra study. The next three weeks were the hardest of my life.

When the big day arrived, I felt confident.

The exam had the same format as the ones I had sat at St Athan, only this time, there would be more emphasis on electronic systems and fault-finding. I was relaxed when I entered the room to sit the multiple-choice paper, and when it was over I was sure I'd passed.

The practical was difficult, but my preparation had been impeccable. After each test, when I talked to some of the other candidates, I felt I was doing well. By the end of the fourth day, my group had completed the practical tests and we were going out. Pass or fail, at that moment it did not matter; it was all over.

Next morning, my group sat in our classroom, bleary-eyed and hungover, anxiously waiting for someone to come in and tell us whether we had passed or failed. It was not long before the head of the Trade Standards and Testing Section entered the room. The head tester was the same chief technician that had tested me at St Athan and who had tested me again at Melksham. He was not frowning, but neither was he smiling, when he said "Good morning."

No one had been called out of the room for a separate

meeting, which was a good sign. The head tester went through the procedure of asking if there were any complaints and if we thought that the tests had been fair. No one complained. A smile came on the chief tester's face. "I have good news for you." Then he hesitated.

I thought, 'Why is it that people who are giving out the results always hesitate before they read them out?'

He continued, "This group has done very well. I can tell you that you have all passed." We all cheered.

After giving us feedback about areas to improve upon, he read out the results. I was in the middle with 76% on the paper test and 70% on the practical. Dave got the top mark. Reg scored higher than me on the paper but received two marks fewer on the practical.

"Right, lads," he said, "You know what to do now. Collect your departure cards and, when they are completed, and you have your rail warrants, you are free to go back to your units." The chief could see that everyone was happy. Some were literally jumping with joy. He turned to leave, and his parting words were, "Well done, all of you. I'll see you again in two years' time when you come for your corporals' exam."

When the chief left the room, we congratulated each other then made a beeline for headquarters to collect our blue cards.

Saying goodbye to my friends was never easy, even though it was and would always be a regular occurrence in the RAF. We promised to keep in touch, but that was not the way it was done in the RAF. There was a good chance we might meet again when posted to a new unit or went on training courses or exercises, but it was not our custom to write each other letters. I said goodbye to Reg and Dave. I was never lucky enough to meet these good friends again.

******

I signed in at the guard room at St Athan and was just in time to get my arrivals card and collect my bedding. I was allocated a bed in the same block, but in a different room to where I'd previously lived.

After dumping my Scotland bag, which was now getting a bit tatty, I relaxed and waited for the others to get back from work. I did not have long to wait.

Davy Maule was in the same room as me, and Tom and Noddy just down the corridor. When I saw Tom, he told me that there was a judo competition the following Sunday. The Leicester Police Club were visiting, and I knew some of their judo players. I had given up new friends, but now I was back amongst old friends and familiar routines; I was happy.

Friday night was fun night, and Davy, Tom and I headed for Llantwit Major. Mr and Mrs Jenkins were pleased to see me at the White Heart. In the past, I'd helped Mrs Jenkins to red lead the floor and steps of the pub. David Jenkins not only ran the pub with his wife, he delivered milk to our workshop at break times. "Welcome back!" he called from behind the bar. "My milk sales will go up now you're back."

It was a good night, but I had to work on Saturday mornings and I knew I would get the third degree when I went to Warrant Officer Rinti Monahan's office to get my arrival card signed.

******

"Well, Carruthers, tell me, how did you get on?"

"I passed, sir," I replied, not sure whether to smile or not.

Rinti smiled. He did not often smile. He said, "Good. Sit down. If you had not passed you would have let 32 MU down and I would have your guts for garters."

I sat down on the chair in front of his desk. Rinti continued, "I will let you know when your promotion comes through. What are your plans now? And I don't mean your social life!"

"I'm not sure," I replied. "I'd like to stay at St Athan and concentrate on my work and sports." This was the answer I thought he wanted to hear.

"Let me give you some good advice," Rinti said in a strong voice. "You have a good future ahead of you if you do the right things and continue to study and work hard, but if you remain at 32 MU you will end up in some godforsaken place like Aden, El-Adam or, worse still, Gan."

I was shocked. I'd never heard him give out this type of advice before.

He continued, "You should think about your future and apply for an overseas posting to one of the better places. You may or may not get your choice. You know by now how the air force works. It could take six months for an overseas posting to come through; but, it will come, and single men are usually the first to get selected for the not-so-nice places, so think about it."

I thanked him for the advice and turned to leave.

"Just a minute," he said. "In the meantime, I am going to move you into the test bay. You need to prove yourself now that you've been promoted. You are going into the test bay to join Chief Technician Walker's group."

The test bay was the cream of all jobs. All I could say was, "Thank you, sir, I won't let you down."

"You'd better not," he replied." With that, he held out his hand and I shook it.

As I walked down the stairs from the office I realised that, despite the hardships, I liked the RAF. I was fully grown-up and had my whole life in front of me. The past did not matter.

CHAPTER 22

The Finale

People often say, "You never forget your roots!" I believe this is true. When I got out of my wife's little yellow car, entered through the lynch gate and looked at the old Kirk cemetery I felt sad. In fact, I felt angry. The cemetery was overgrown and in disrepair. I struggled through the thick, wet grass and peered through the heavy iron gate into the mausoleum. Tears mixed with rain ran down my cheeks. The plaques on the walls were damaged and very dirty. No one had been in there and done any maintenance for years. I got in the car and headed home.

Five years later, I came to Annan to visit family and enjoy the annual festival of the Riding of the Marches. I decided to visit Cummertrees and take some photographs. As I walked through the village taking snaps I thought I'd better tell someone why I was photographing the village hall and the rows of cottages. With the laws as they are today I thought, 'If I don't tell someone what I'm doing, I may get arrested.'

The only people I could see was a couple from the second cottage in from the church. They were tending their garden. As I approached I said, "Excuse me, if you are wondering why I'm taking photographs, it's for my memoirs."

The man stood up and said, "If it's memories you want, I've lived here all my life. I am the longest-living resident, so if you need to know anything about the village, I can tell you."

I thought that I must know him, so I said, "What's your name?"

He looked at me carefully and said, "Henry Dobie."

I felt happy. I said, "I am Drew."

I did not get a chance to say 'Carruthers'. Henry put his

arms around my shoulders and uttered, "Drew, it's good to see you."

The next hour was spent reminiscing. It felt good.

As I walked towards the church, a car was parked outside the lynch gate. I had been told that when the church was sold the new owner had done it up and was now letting it out as a holiday home. I asked the gentleman if he was on holiday and he replied, "No, I'm the owner." I was anxious to talk to him, but I could see that he was busy. What I did learn was that, with great difficulty, he had tried to carry out maintenance work in the old cemetery, but he found it hard to make any real progress. When I looked around, I thought that the cemetery was looking a lot tidier than it had done five years previously, when I'd last visited.

Three-quarters of a century is a long time, but I have never forgotten those wonderful memories of my early life at Cummertrees. I would say to all those new people who have moved to live there, "Thank you for taking care of my wonderful village."

EPILOGUE

When I look at people's attitude to illegitimacy today, I can tell there has been a great deal of progress made to get rid of the discrimination that mothers and children like me suffered for years before and after I was born. Thankfully, an illegitimate child today is no longer looked upon as an unwanted child, a sinner or someone with whom other children should not play.

I hope that my grandson now realises that he is not all that different to me. And now he knows the stories from when I was young.

I think that the Royal Air Force deserves credit for taking young people, like me and many others, who came from broken homes and making us into what we are today. There was a price I had to pay for this, and that price was the abuse and bullying that boy entrants had to endure.

Many times I have heard people say phrases like 'Bring back National Service', and 'Discipline makes the man'. I can honestly say that the discipline I endured did not make me a 'man'. What I think made me into what I am today was the technical training, the comradeship, teamwork and self-discipline that I learned.

Excluding my Boy service, I served 12 years and 248 days. I didn't count the minutes. I recall that when I first joined the RAF, Chief Technician Turner told me that I could make his rank after about 15 years. At that time, I could not see me making it to the end of my boy entrant training and 15 years seemed like a lifetime. I did make it, and when I left the service I was a sergeant and had passed the tests to become a chief technician. I was 31 years old, having served mainly in Bomber Command in the UK, with tours in Malta, Cyprus and Libya.

The best project I worked on was the conversion of the

Victor Bomber to an in-flight refuelling tanker. I was part of this small team of people who worked seven days a week, 12 hours a day, to make the project a success.

I never used my weapons training, but I did get shot. Around 6:00a.m. one day I was riding my bicycle to switch off the security lights at Taqali in Malta. As I cycled across the airfield, a local poacher opened fire at a bird that had been disturbed. He missed the bird but some of the pellets hit me and I fell off my bike. No harm done; I let him off with a warning.

My proudest moment was accepting the queen's shilling, which I still have.

I had a good career and, when I left the RAF, I found it difficult to settle down. My first job was at Ferranti in Edinburgh as a calibration engineer. I liked the job, but it was a factory and I did not like being enclosed. I left when I was offered a job as a trainer at a group training centre in Grangemouth, followed by another job working for the government – again, as a trainer.

I think it was luck when I got word that, because of policy changes, I was to be made redundant. It was luck again when I saw a job advert for engineers and senior foremen who were wanted for a three-year contract in Kuwait. I applied and, a few weeks later, I ended up working for the Kuwait Oil Company.

I gained a lot of experience working within the petrochemical industry in Kuwait for five years. No doubt that experience helped me get my next, and many more, contracts working both on-shore and off-shore in the oil industry - including ten years in Malaysia and five years in China. What was my job? Training young people who were not much older than myself when I left the Boy Entrants.

ACKNOWLEDGEMENTS

Royal Airforce Boy Entrants Association, for information and advice

Brian Carlin, author of The Boy Entrant, for guidance and advice

Passing out Parade photograph courtesy of the '91st Entry RAF Locking Apprentices website'

Billet photograph courtesy of AWF 72 website

Cosford Air Museum, for their help with my research

Annan and Dumfries Museum, for their help with my research

Annandale Observer, for their help and advice

The Writers Bureau; in particular, Nicola Lisle, for her patience and feedback

The Writing Hall, for guiding me through the final stages

The people of Cummertrees and Annan who gave advice and information

Graeme Allister – Cummertrees Church, for his efforts in cleaning up the old cemetery and supplying photographs

Wikimedia Commons, for the church image

Victor Bomber by Arpingstone - Own work, Public Domain:

https://commons.wikimedia.org/w/index.php?curid=5155052

APPENDIX 1

Old Units used in the UK before decimalisation and Metrification

Money

How did the pre-decimal system work?

There were three units of currency: the penny, the shilling and the pound. There were 12 pence in a shilling and 20 shillings in a pound. So, 12 x 20 = 240 pence in a pound.

2 farthings = 1 halfpenny pronounced 'hapepenny' = 0.208p

4 farthings = 1 penny (d) Latin – denarius = 0.417p

3 pennies = 1 threepenny bit = 1.25p

6 pennies = 1 sixpenny piece = 2.5p

12 pennies = 1 shilling(s), a bob as in 'bob a job' = 5p

2 shillings = 1 florin, a tenth of a pound = 10p

2s - 6d; 2/6d = 1 half-crown, biggest coin in regular use = 12.5p

10 shillings = 1 ten 'bob' note first in paper money = 50p

20 shillings = 1 pound note (quid) also £5 and £10 notes

= £1Imperial - UK Units of Length

1 inch (in. or ") = about the width of a thumb = 25.4 mm

12 inches (ins.) = 1 foot about the length of a size 10 shoe = 305 mm

3 feet (ft.) = 1 yard about from nose to stretched finger = 0.91 m

1760 yards (yds) = 1 mile (m) about 15 minutes walking =

1.61 km

Imperial - UK units of Area

144 square inch (sq.in) = 1 sq.foot about a paper napkin = 0.093 m2

9 square feet (sq.ft) = 1 sq.yard about the size of a card table = 0.84 m2

4840 sq.yards (sq.yds) = 1 acre about a football pitch = 4047 m2

Imperial - UK units of Mass or Weight

16 drams (dr) = 1 ounce a tablespoon of sugar = 28 grams

16 ounces (ozs.) = 1 pound a bag of sugar = 0.45 kg

14 pounds (lbs) = 1 stone used in body weight = 6.35 kg

1 hundredweight = 112 lb; bag of cement. = 50.8 kg

20 hundredweight (cwt) = 1 ton = 2240 lb.; about 14 men = 1.016 tonne

Imperial - UK units of Capacity

5 fluid ounces = 1 gill = 142 ml

20 fluid ounces = 1 pint an English beer = 568 ml

2 pints (pts.) = 1 quart a German beer = 1.1 L

4 quarts (qrt) = 1 gallon; a large can of paint, maybe = 4.546 L

APPENDIX 2

The following is an extract from the regulations covering Pay and Conditions of Service at that time.

NOTES ON PAY AND THE
BOY ENTRANT SAVING SCHEME

1. It is very important that boys learn something of the value of money, and acquire a "money sense" during their training. To this end, special facilities are available for the Boy Entrants to save and otherwise conserve a proportion of their pay every week.

Pay

2. The rates of pay which boys receive during training, are given below, but only a portion of this sum is handed to the boys weekly, as "pocket money". The balance is retained by the Accountant Officer and paid out to the boys when they go on leave or half-term break. The standard <u>daily</u> rates of pay, and <u>weekly</u> money issued to the boys are as follows: -

(a) <u>Rates of Pay</u>

    (i)   On Arrival   6/..d. per day
    (ii)   Second Year 7/6d. per day
    (iii) At 17 years   10/6d. per day

    (iv) At 17½ years 18/6d. per day

(b) <u>Weekly Issue</u>

    (i) Whilst in Initial Training Squadron – 15/..d.

(3 months approx.)

(ii)　After initial training until they become Senior Entry, 15/..d. to £1-5-0d.

(c) A boy's pay is dealt with in the following manner:-

Weekly pay:-	15/..0d
Post Office Savings:-	3/6d.
Retained as credit :-	20/..d.
Incidental Charges:-	3/5d.

(Insurance, etc.)

We here consider that 15/..d, is sufficient weekly pocket money for a boy and experience shows this amount to be sufficient. The Post Office Savings Book is retained by us until leave comes along when it is given to the boy so he may draw from it if necessary. On the pay day prior to leave a boy is paid all his credit together with full pay and ration allowance for the period of leave, thus ensuring that boys are taught to save and to have more than sufficient funds to cover their leave.

<u>Allowances</u>

3.　In addition to their pay, boys also receive a Ration Allowance and a Clothing Allowance. The Ration Allowance, which varies with the cost of living is given in kind except when boys go on leave, when they receive their entitlement in cash up to a maximum of 42 days per year. The present rate of ration allowance is 6/2d. per day.

4.　Clothing Allowance 7¼d. per day is admissible after 6 months' service.

<u>Saving</u>

5.   In order to encourage a proper sense of money value all boys are expected to save voluntarily. On arrival they are asked to sign a savings form and thereafter the amount is automatically credited to their to their Post Office Savings Account every week. The rates of Saving, which can be maintained in relation to the boys rate of pay have been carefully worked out, and they vary between 6d. per day on arrival to 4/..d. a day for boys over 17½ years of age.

6.   For this scheme to be of value it is essential that boys do not make unnecessary withdrawals from their accounts. Arrangements have therefore been made for Post Office Savings books to be deposited with the boys Flight Commanders. In this way the books are safeguarded against loss and the Flight Commanders can advise the boys on withdrawals and help to develop their money sense.

7.   It is hoped that all parents will co-operate with the school in maintaining a satisfactory standard of saving; by encouraging their sons to make full use of the advice and facilities which are available to him.